Applied Calculus

Fourth Edition

Michigan State University

Wiley Custom Learning Solutions

CUSTOM BRIEF CONTENTS

1   FUNCTIONS AND CHANGE   1

2   RATE OF CHANGE: THE DERIVATIVE   87

3   SHORTCUTS TO DIFFERENTIATION   133

4   USING THE DERIVATIVE   169

5   ACCUMULATED CHANGE: THE DEFINITE INTEGRAL   233

6   USING THE DEFINITE INTEGRAL   275

7   ANTIDERIVATIVES   299

8   PROBABILITY   327

9   FUNCTIONS OF SEVERAL VARIABLES   349

10   MATHEMATICAL MODELING USING DIFFERENTIAL
     EQUATIONS   403

11   GEOMETRIC SERIES   453

APPENDICES

A   FITTING FORMULAS TO DATA   472

B   COMPOUND INTEREST AND THE NUMBER e 480

C   SPREADSHEET PROJECTS   485

ANSWERS TO ODD-NUMBERED PROBLEMS   495

PRETEST   521

INDEX   525

APPENDIX B: MTH 124 – SAMPLE FINAL EXAM   1

FORMULA SUMMARY: ALGEBRA

Lines

Slope of line through (x_1, y_1) and (x_2, y_2):

$$m = \frac{y_2 - y_1}{x_2 - x_1}$$

Point-slope equation of line through (x_1, y_1) with slope m:

$$y - y_1 = m(x - x_1)$$

Slope-intercept equation of line with slope m and y-intercept b:

$$y = b + mx$$

Definition of Zero, Negative, and Fractional Exponents

$$a^0 = 1, \quad a^{-1} = \frac{1}{a}, \quad \text{and, in general, } a^{-x} = \frac{1}{a^x}$$

$$a^{1/2} = \sqrt{a}, \quad a^{1/3} = \sqrt[3]{a}, \quad \text{and, in general, } a^{1/n} = \sqrt[n]{a}.$$

$$\text{Also, } a^{m/n} = \sqrt[n]{a^m} = (\sqrt[n]{a})^m.$$

Rules of Exponents

1. $a^x \cdot a^t = a^{x+t}$ For example, $2^4 \cdot 2^3 = (2 \cdot 2 \cdot 2 \cdot 2) \cdot (2 \cdot 2 \cdot 2) = 2^7$.

2. $\dfrac{a^x}{a^t} = a^{x-t}$ For example, $\dfrac{2^4}{2^3} = \dfrac{2 \cdot 2 \cdot 2 \cdot 2}{2 \cdot 2 \cdot 2} = 2^1$.

3. $(a^x)^t = a^{xt}$ For example, $(2^3)^2 = 2^3 \cdot 2^3 = 2^6$.

Definition of Natural Log

$y = \ln x$ means $e^y = x$; *for example:* $\ln 1 = 0$, since $e^0 = 1$.

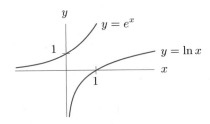

Rules of Natural Logarithms

$$\ln(AB) = \ln A + \ln B$$

$$\ln\left(\frac{A}{B}\right) = \ln A - \ln B$$

$$\ln A^p = p \ln A$$

Identities

$$\ln e^x = x$$

$$e^{\ln x} = x$$

Exponential function: $y = P_0 a^x$

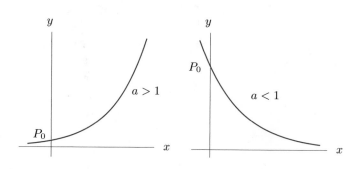

Logarithm function: $y = \ln x$

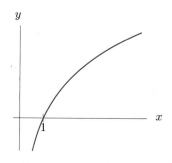

Periodic functions

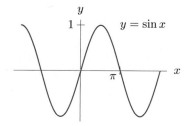

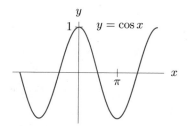

Logistic function: $y = \dfrac{L}{1 + Ce^{-kx}}$

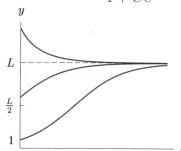

Surge function: $y = axe^{-bx}$

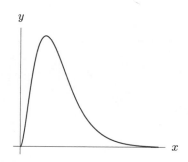

APPLIED CALCULUS

Fourth Edition

APPLIED CALCULUS

Fourth Edition

Produced by the Calculus Consortium and initially funded by a National Science Foundation Grant.

Deborah Hughes-Hallett
University of Arizona

William G. McCallum
University of Arizona

Andrew M. Gleason
Harvard University

Brad G. Osgood
Stanford University

Patti Frazer Lock
St. Lawrence University

Douglas Quinney
University of Keele

Daniel E. Flath
Macalester College

Karen Rhea
University of Michigan

David O. Lomen
University of Arizona

Jeff Tecosky-Feldman
Haverford College

David Lovelock
University of Arizona

Thomas W. Tucker
Colgate University

with the assistance of

Otto K. Bretscher
Colby College

Eric Connally
Harvard Extension School

Richard D. Porter
Northeastern University

Sheldon P. Gordon
SUNY at Farmingdale

Andrew Pasquale
Chelmsford High School

Joe B. Thrash
University of Southern Mississippi

Coordinated by
Elliot J. Marks

WILEY

John Wiley & Sons, Inc.

PUBLISHER	Laurie Rosatone
ACQUISITIONS EDITOR	David Dietz
ASSOCIATE EDITOR	Shannon Corliss
EDITORIAL ASSISTANT	Pamela Lashbrook
DEVELOPMENTAL EDITOR	Anne Scanlan-Rohrer/Two Ravens Editorial
MARKETING MANAGER	Sarah Davis
MEDIA EDITOR	Melissa Edwards
SENIOR PRODUCTION EDITOR	Ken Santor
COVER DESIGNER	Madelyn Lesure
COVER AND CHAPTER OPENING PHOTO	©Patrick Zephyr/Patrick Zephyr Nature Photography Images

Problems from *Calculus: The Analysis of Functions*, by Peter D. Taylor (Toronto: Wall & Emerson, Inc., 1992). Reprinted with permission of the publisher.

This book was set in Times Roman by the Consortium using TeX, Mathematica, and the package AsTeX, which was written by Alex Kasman. It was printed and bound by R.R. Donnelley / Jefferson City. The cover was printed by R.R. Donnelley.

This book is printed on acid-free paper.

This material is based upon work supported by the National Science Foundation under Grant No. DUE-9352905. Opinions expressed are those of the authors and not necessarily those of the Foundation.

ISBN: 978-0-470-17052-6
Binder Ready: 978-0-470-55662-7

Printed in the United States of America

10 9 8 7 6 5 4

We dedicate this book to Andrew M. Gleason.

His brilliance and the extraordinary kindness and dignity with which he treated others made an enormous difference to us, and to many, many people. Andy brought out the best in everyone.

> *Deb Hughes Hallett*
> *for the Calculus Consortium*

PREFACE

Calculus is one of the greatest achievements of the human intellect. Inspired by problems in astronomy, Newton and Leibniz developed the ideas of calculus 300 years ago. Since then, each century has demonstrated the power of calculus to illuminate questions in mathematics, the physical sciences, engineering, and the social and biological sciences.

Calculus has been so successful because of its extraordinary power to reduce complicated problems to simple rules and procedures. Therein lies the danger in teaching calculus: it is possible to teach the subject as nothing but the rules and procedures—thereby losing sight of both the mathematics and of its practical value. This edition of *Applied Calculus* continues our effort to promote courses in which understanding reinforces computation.

Origin of the Text: A Community of Instructors

This text, like others we write, draws on the experience of a diverse group of authors and users. We have benefitted enormously from input from a broad spectrum of instructors—at research universities, four-year colleges, community colleges, and secondary schools. For *Applied Calculus*, the contributions of colleagues in biology, economics, medicine, business, and other life and social sciences have been equally central to the development of the text. It is the collective wisdom of this community of mathematicians, teachers, natural and social scientists that forms the basis for the new edition.

A Balance Between Skills and Concepts

The first edition of our text struck a new balance between concepts and skills. As instructors ourselves, we know that the balance we choose depends on the students we have: sometimes a focus on conceptual understanding is best; sometimes more drill is appropriate. The flexibility of this new fourth edition allows instructors to tailor the course to their students.

Since 1992, we have continued to find new ways to help students learn. Under our approach, which we call the "Rule of Four," ideas are presented graphically, numerically, symbolically, and verbally, thereby encouraging students with a variety of learning styles to expand their knowledge. Our problems probe student understanding in areas often taken for granted. The influence of these problems, praised for their creativity and variety, has extended far beyond the users of our textbook.

Mathematical Thinking: A Balance Between Theory and Modeling

The first stage in the development of mathematical thinking is the acquisition of a clear intuitive picture of the central ideas. In the next stage, the student learns to reason with the intuitive ideas and explain the reasoning clearly in plain English. After this foundation has been laid, there is a choice of direction. All students benefit from both theory and modeling, but the balance may differ for different groups. In our experience as instructors, students of this book are motivated both by understanding the concepts and by seeing the power of mathematics applied to their fields of interest—be it the spread of a disease or the analysis of a company. Some instructors may choose a more theoretical approach; others may choose to ground the mathematics in applied examples. This text is flexible enough to support both approaches.

Mathematical Skills: A Balance Between Symbolic Manipulation and Technology

To use calculus effectively, students need skill in both symbolic manipulation and the use of technology. The balance between them may vary, depending on the needs of the students and the wishes of the instructor. The book is adaptable to many different combinations.

The book does not require any specific software or technology. It has been used with graphing calculators, graphing software, and computer algebra systems. Any technology with the ability to graph functions and perform numerical integration will suffice. Students are expected to use their own judgment to determine where technology is useful.

What Student Background is Expected?

This book is intended for students in business, the social sciences, and the life sciences. We have found the material to be thought-provoking for well-prepared students while still accessible to students with weak algebra backgrounds. Providing numerical and graphical approaches as well as the algebraic gives students several ways of mastering the material. This approach encourages students to persist, thereby lowering failure rate; a pre-test over background material is available in the appendix to the book; An algebra refresher is avalable at the student book companion site at www.wiley.com/college/hughes-hallett.

The Fourth Edition: Expanded Options

Because different users often choose very different topics to cover in a one-semester applied calculus course, we have designed this book for either a one-semester course (with much flexibility in choosing topics) or a two-semester course. Sample syllabi are provided in the Instructor's Manual.

The fourth edition has the same vision as the first three editions. In preparing this edition, we solicited comments from a large number of mathematicians who had used the text. We continued to discuss with our colleagues in client disciplines the mathematical needs of their students. We were offered many valuable suggestions, which we have tried to incorporate, while maintaining our original commitment to a focused treatment of a limited number of topics. The changes we have made include:

- **Updated data** and **fresh applications** throughout the book.
- Many **new problems** have been added. These have been designed to build student confidence with basic concepts and to reinforce skills.
- **Chapter 1 has been shortened**; the material on polynomials has been streamlined to focus on quadratics. Focus sections have been moved to the appendix or removed.
- Material on **relative change** and **relative rates of change** has been added in Sections 1.3, 2.3, and 3.3, thereby allowing instructors to reinforce the distinction between rates of change and relative rates of change.
- A new **project on relative growth rates in economics** has been added in Chapter 3.
- A new section on **integration by parts** has been added to Chapter 7.
- True-False **Check Your Understanding** questions have been added at the end of every chapter, enabling students to check their progress.
- As in the previous edition, a **Pre-test** is included for students whose skills may need a refresher prior to taking the course.
- **Pointers** have been inserted in chapters referring students to Appendices or Focus sections.

Content

This content represents our vision of how applied calculus can be taught. It is flexible enough to accommodate individual course needs and requirements. Topics can easily be added or deleted, or the order changed.

Chapter 1: Functions and Change

Chapter 1 introduces the concept of a function and the idea of change, including the distinction between total change, rate of change, and relative change. All elementary functions are introduced here. Although the functions are probably familiar, the graphical, numerical, verbal, and modeling approach to them is likely to be new. We introduce exponential functions early, since they are fundamental to the understanding of real-world processes.

Chapter 2: Rate of Change: The Derivative

Chapter 2 presents the key concept of the derivative according to the Rule of Four. The purpose of this chapter is to give the student a practical understanding of the meaning of the derivative and its interpretation as an instantaneous rate of change. Students will learn how the derivative can be used to represent relative rates of change. After finishing this chapter, a student will be able to approximate derivatives numerically by taking difference quotients, visualize derivatives graphically as the slope of the graph, and interpret the meaning of first and second derivatives in various applications. The student will also understand the concept of marginality and recognize the derivative as a function in its own right.

Focus on Theory: This section discusses limits and continuity and presents the symbolic definition of the derivative.

Chapter 3: Short-Cuts to Differentiation

The derivatives of all the functions in Chapter 1 are introduced, as well as the rules for differentiating products, quotients, and composite functions. Students learn how to find relative rates of change using logarithms.

Focus on Theory: This section uses the definition of the derivative to obtain the differentiation rules.

Focus on Practice: This section provides a collection of differentiation problems for skill-building.

Chapter 4: Using the Derivative

The aim of this chapter is to enable the student to use the derivative in solving problems, including optimization and graphing. It is not necessary to cover all the sections.

Chapter 5: Accumulated Change: The Definite Integral

Chapter 5 presents the key concept of the definite integral, in the same spirit as Chapter 2.

The purpose of this chapter is to give the student a practical understanding of the definite integral as a limit of Riemann sums, and to bring out the connection between the derivative and the definite integral in the Fundamental Theorem of Calculus. We use the same method as in Chapter 2, introducing the fundamental concept in depth without going into technique. The student will finish the chapter with a good grasp of the definite integral as a limit of Riemann sums, and the ability to approximate a definite integral numerically and interpret it graphically. The chapter includes applications of definite iintegrals in a variety of contexts.

Chapter 5 can be covered immediately after Chapter 2 without difficulty.

Focus on Theory: This section presents the Second Fundamental Theorem of Calculus and the properties of the definite integral.

Chapter 6: Using the Definite Integral

This chapter presents applications of the definite integral. It is not meant to be comprehensive and it is not necessary to cover all the sections.

Chapter 7: Antiderivatives

This chapter covers antiderivatives from a graphical, numerical, and algebraic point of view. Sections on integration by substitution and integration by parts are included. The Fundamental Theorem of Calculus is used to evaluate definite integrals and to analyze antiderivatives.

Focus on Practice: This section provides a collection of integration problems for skill-building.

Chapter 8: Probability

This chapter covers probability density functions, cumulative distribution functions, the median, and the mean.

Chapter 9: Functions of Several Variables

Chapter 9 introduces functions of two variables from several points of view, using contour diagrams, formulas, and tables. It gives students the skills to read contour diagrams and think graphically, to read tables and think numerically, and to apply these skills, along with their algebraic skills, to modeling. The idea of the partial derivative is introduced from graphical, numerical, and symbolic viewpoints. Partial derivatives are then applied to optimization problems, ending with a discussion of constrained optimization using Lagrange multipliers.

Focus on Theory: This section uses optimization to derive the formula for the regression line.

Chapter 10: Mathematical Modeling Using Differential Equations

This chapter introduces differential equations. The emphasis is on modeling, qualitative solutions, and interpretation. This chapter includes applications of systems of differential equations to population models, the spread of disease, and predator-prey interactions.

Focus on Theory: This section explains the technique of separation of variables.

Chapter 11: Geometric Series

This chapter covers geometric series and their applications to business, economics, and the life sciences.

Appendices

The first appendix introduces the student to fitting formulas to data; the second appendix provides further discussion of compound interest and the definition of the number e. The third appendix contains a selection of spreadsheet projects.

Supplementary Materials

Supplements for the instructor can be obtained by sending a request on your institutional letterhead to Mathematics Marketing Manager, John Wiley & Sons Inc., 111 River Street, Hoboken, NJ 07030-5774, or by contacting your local Wiley representative. The following supplementary materials are available.

- **Instructor's Manual** (ISBN 978-0-470-60189-1) containing teaching tips, sample syllabii, calculator programs, and overhead transparency masters.
- **Instructor's Solution Manual** (ISBN 978-0-470-60190-7) with complete solutions to all problems.
- **Student's Solution Manual** (ISBN 978-0-470-17053-3) with complete solutions to half the odd-numbered problems.
- **Student Study Guide** (ISBN 978-0-470-45820-4) with additional study aids for students that are tied directly to the book.
- **Additional Material for Instructors**, elaborating specially marked points in the text, as well as password protected electronic versions of the instructor ancillaries, can be found on the web at www.wiley.com/college/hughes-hallett.
- **Additional Material for Students**, at the student book companion site at www.wiley.com/college/hughes-hallett, includes an algebra refresher and web quizzes.

Getting Started Technology Manual Series:

- **Getting Started with Mathematica**, 3rd edn, by C-K. Cheung, G.E. Keough, Robert H. Gross, and Charles Landraitis of Boston College (ISBN 978-0-470-45687-3)
- **Getting Started with Maple**, 3rd edn, by C-K. Cheung, G.E. Keough, both of Boston College, and Michael May of St. Louis University (ISBN 978-0-470-45554-8)

ConcepTests

ConcepTests, (ISBN 978-0-470-60191-4) modeled on the pioneering work of Harvard physicist Eric Mazur, are questions designed to promote active learning during class, particularly (but not exclusively) in large lectures. Evaluation data shows that students taught with ConcepTests outperformed students taught by traditional lecture methods 73% versus 17% on conceptual questions, and 63% versus 54% on computational problems.[1] A new supplement to *Applied Calculus*, 4th edn, containing ConcepTests by section, is available from your Wiley representative.

Wiley Faculty Network

The Wiley Faculty Network is a peer-to-peer network of academic faculty dedicated to the effective use of technology in the classroom. This group can help you apply innovative classroom techniques and implement specific software packages. Visit www.wherefacultyconnect.com or ask your Wiley representative for details.

WileyPLUS

WileyPLUS, Wiley's digital learning environment, is loaded with all of the supplements above, and also features:

- E-book, which is an exact version of the print text, but also features hyperlinks to questions, definitions, and supplements for quicker and easier support.

- Homework management tools, which easily enable the instructor to assign and automatically grade questions, using a rich set of options and controls.

- QuickStart pre-designed reading and homework assignments. Use them as-is or customize them to fit the needs of your classroom.

- Guided Online (GO) Exercises, which prompt students to build solutions step-by-step. Rather than simply grading an exercise answer as wrong, GO problems show students precisely where they are making a mistake.

- Student Study Guide, providing key ideas, additional worked examples with corresponding exercises, and study skills.

- Algebra & Trigonometry Refresher quizzes, which provide students with an opportunity to brush-up on material necessary to master calculus, as well as to determine areas that require further review.

- Graphing Calculator Manual, to help students get the most out of their graphing calculator, and to show how they can apply the numerical and graphing functions of their calculators to their study of calculus.

Acknowledgements

First and foremost, we want to express our appreciation to the National Science Foundation for their faith in our ability to produce a revitalized calculus curriculum and, in particular, to Louise Raphael, John Kenelly, John Bradley, Bill Haver, and James Lightbourne. We also want to thank the members of our Advisory Board, Benita Albert, Lida Barrett, Bob Davis, Lovenia DeConge-Watson, John Dossey, Ron Douglas, Don Lewis, Seymour Parter, John Prados, and Steve Rodi for their ongoing guidance and advice.

In addition, we want to thank all the people across the country who encouraged us to write this book and who offered so many helpful comments. We would like to thank the following people, for all that they have done to help our project succeed: Lauren Akers, Ruth Baruth, Jeffery Bergen, Ted Bick, Graeme Bird, Kelly Boyle, Kelly Brooks, Lucille Buonocore, R.B. Burckel, J. Curtis Chipman, Dipa Choudhury, Scott Clark, Larry Crone, Jane Devoe, Jeff Edmunds, Gail Ferrell, Joe Fiedler, Holland Filgo, Sally Fischbeck, Ron Frazer, Lynn Garner, David Graser, Ole Hald, Jenny Harrison, John Hennessey, Yvette Hester, David Hornung, Richard Iltis, Adrian Iovita, Jerry Johnson, Thomas Judson, Selin Kalaycioglu, Bonnie Kelly, Mary Kittell, Donna Krawczyk, Theodore Laetsch, T.-Y. Lam, Sylvain Laroche, Kurt Lemmert, Suzanne Lenhart,

---

[1]"Peer Instruction in Physics and Mathematics" by Scott Pilzer in *Primus*, Vol XI, No 2, June 2001. At the start of Calculus II, students earned 73% on conceptual questions and 63% on computational questions if they were taught with ConcepTests in Calculus I; 17% and 54% otherwise.

Madelyn Lesure, Ben Levitt, Thomas Lucas, Alfred Manaster, Peter McClure, Georgia Kamvosoulis Mederer, Kurt Mederer, David Meredith, Nolan Miller, Mohammad Moazzam, Saadat Moussavi, Patricia Oakley, Mary Ellen O'Leary, Jim Osterburg, Mary Parker, Ruth Parsons, Greg Peters, Kim Presser, Sarah Richardson, Laurie Rosatone, Daniel Rovey, Harry Row, Kenneth Santor, Anne Scanlan-Rohrer, Alfred Schipke, Adam Spiegler, Virginia Stallings, Brian Stanley, Mary Jane Sterling, Robert Styer, "Suds" Sudholz, Ralph Teixeira, Thomas Timchek, Jake Thomas, J. Jerry Uhl, Tilaka Vijithakumara, Alan Weinstein, Rachel Deyette Werkema, Aaron Wootton, Hung-Hsi Wu, and Sam Xu.

Reports from the following reviewers were most helpful in shaping the third edition:

Victor Akatsa, Carol Blumberg, Mary Ann Collier, Murray Eisenberg, Donna Fatheree, Dan Fuller, Ken Hannsgen, Marek Kossowski, Sheri Lehavi, Deborah Lurie, Jan Mays, Jeffery Meyer, Bobra Palmer, Barry Peratt, Russ Potter, Ken Price, Maijian Qian, Emily Roth, Lorenzo Traldi, Joan Weiss, Christos Xenophontos.

Reports from the following reviewers were most helpful in shaping the second edition:

Victor Akatsa, Carol Blumberg, Jennifer Fowler, Helen Hancock, Ken Hannsgen, John Haverhals, Mako E. Haruta, Linda Hill, Thom Kline, Jill Messer Lamping, Dennis Lewandowski, Lige Li, William O. Martin, Ted Marsden, Michael Mocciola, Maijian Qian, Joyce Quella, Peter Penner, Barry Peratt, Emily Roth, Jerry Schuur, Barbara Shabell, Peter Sternberg, Virginia Stover, Bruce Yoshiwara, Katherine Yoshiwara.

Deborah Hughes-Hallett	David O. Lomen	Douglas Quinney
Andrew M. Gleason	David Lovelock	Karen Rhea
Patti Frazer Lock	William G. McCallum	Jeff Tecosky-Feldman
Daniel E. Flath	Brad G. Osgood	Thomas W. Tucker

APPLICATIONS INDEX

Business and Economics

Admission fees 35

Advertising 6, 78, 109, 113, 353, 370, 390

Aircraft landing/takeoff 46

Airline capacity and revenue 116–117, 342, 350, 359, 364, 370

Annual interest rate 54, 58, 84, 107, 109, 122, 144, 151, 288, 295, 353, 389, 422, 430, 442–443, 469

Annual yield 297–298

Annuity 459–460, 462, 469

Attendance 23, 67, 194

Average cost 196–201, 225, 229–230, 296

Bank account 55–56, 84, 144, 151, 160–161, 286–287, 295, 350, 353, 375, 389, 406–407, 419, 422, 430, 442–445, 458, 462–463, 467

Beef consumption 207, 352–353, 369

Beer production 75, 370

Bicycle production 23, 263

Bonds 288, 462

Break–even point 30, 35–36

Budget constraints 34, 38, 381–383, 385–388, 393, 395–396

Business revenue
General Motors 25
Hershey 44, 108, 295
McDonald's 13, 289

Car payments 54, 109, 390, 468

Car rental 13, 78, 351–352, 375

Cartel pricing 283

Chemical costs 93, 106–107, 120

Cobb–Douglas production function 195, 201, 357–358, 375, 387–388, 391–392, 394

Coffee 56–57, 78, 123, 160, 256, 369, 381, 393, 407, 427–428

College savings account 295

Competing businesses 435

Compound interest 23, 43, 49, 53–56, 58–59, 81, 84–85, 107, 122, 144, 161, 286–289, 295, 350–351, 419, 422, 430, 442–445, 455–456, 459–462, 467–469

Consols 468

Consumer surplus 280–286, 294, 296

Consumption
calorie 68, 207, 140, 368–369, 395, 443
CFC 5
drug 220
fossil fuel 80, 239, 257, 266, 464–466, 469
energy 124, 280, 323
gas in car 122, 147, 162, 184

Consumption smoothing 279

Contract negotiation 58, 467

Cost function 27–29, 31, 35–36, 61, 79, 83, 115–116, 118, 140, 146, 190, 194, 196–200, 224–225, 229, 261–263, 269, 296, 304, 381, 388, 394

Cost overruns 345

Coupon 462

Crop yields 77, 140, 186, 297–298, 332, 422–423

Demand curve 31–32, 35–38, 67, 69, 80, 83, 1140, 145, 153, 203, 280–286, 294, 296, 304

Density function 328–346

Depreciation 4, 8, 31, 58, 80, 408

Doubling time 50, 52, 54, 56–58, 84

Duality 396

Economy 27, 70, 358, 394, 461, 463, 468, 470

Economy of scale 115

Elasticity of demand 202–207, 225, 229

Energy output and consumption 45, 56, 105, 122, 239, 257, 280, 295, 316, 323, 466–467

Equilibrium prices 32–34, 36–39, 80, 83, 280–286, 294, 296

Equilibrium solution 423, 426–427, 430–433, 441, 443–444, 446, 466

Farms in the US 17, 92–93

Fertilizer use 7, 77, 104, 140, 338

Fixed cost 27–28, 30, 35–37, 61, 79, 115, 190–191, 193–195, 197, 201, 224–225, 262–263, 266, 269, 304

Future value 54–56, 58, 84, 286–289, 295–296, 415

Gains from trade 283–286, 296

Gas mileage 7, 147, 184, 353, 395

Gold production and reserves 122

Government spending 34, 107, 461, 463, 468

Gross World Product 50

Gross Domestic Product 3, 27, 44, 106, 164

Harrod–Hicks model 470

Heating costs 277

Households,
with cableTV 25, 94, 225–226
with PCs 122

Housing construction 70

Income stream 286–288, 295–296

Inflation 27, 45, 54, 151, 159

Interest 6, 23, 49, 53, 56, 58–59, 69, 81, 84–85, 107, 109, 122, 144, 151, 161, 286–289, 295–296, 350, 353, 369–371, 375, 389–391, 406–407, 419, 422, 430, 442–445, 455–456, 459–460, 462, 468–469

Inventory 279, 294, 338

Investments 6, 45, 54, 58, 173–174, 261, 288, 295, 350, 358, 392–394, 408, 444, 456

Job growth rates 292

Joint cost function 388, 394

Labor force 25, 358, 362, 373, 387–388, 392

Land use 214, 423

Lifetime
of a banana 338, 343
of a machine 331
of a transistor 339

Loan payments 58, 69, 85, 109, 279, 295, 370, 390

Lottery payments 55, 58

Machine payments 31, 59, 289

Manufacturing 27, 36, 93, 194, 231–232, 292, 378, 388, 392–393

Marginal cost 27–28, 31, 35–36, 79, 83, 103, 115–120, 125, 140, 145–146, 188–194, 196–201, 207, 223, 224, 228–230, 261–263, 266, 269, 304

Marginal product of labor 195

Marginal profit 31, 36, 83, 189, 229, 263

Marginal revenue 31, 35–36, 83, 116–120, 125, 140, 151, 153, 188–194, 196, 207, 223, 228–229, 263, 304

Market stabilization point 461–2, 468

Maximum profit 188–191, 194–196, 207, 224, 229, 378–379, 351, 394

Maximum revenue 67, 192, 194, 204

Milk production 13, 205, 283

Money circulation 461–462

Mortgage payments 69, 123, 353, 369

Multiplier 104, 107, 141, 455, 42

Multiplier, Lagrange 383, 385–389, 394–395

Multiplier effect 461, 463

Multiplier, fiscal policy 107

Mutual funds 108, 240

Net worth of a company 263, 404–405, 425–426, 436

Phone rates 13, 22, 24, 206, 345

Photocopy reduction 46

Point of diminishing returns 210, 213–214, 226

Present value 54–56, 58, 84, 286–289, 295–296, 357, 460, 462, 467–469

Price control 283, 285

Pricing 13, 283, 350

Producer surplus 281–282, 284–285,294–295

Production costs 36, 388, 392

Production function 195, 231, 357–358, 373, 375, 382, 386–388, 391–396

Production workers 95

Productivity 77

Profit function 30–31, 36, 189–192, 379

Railway passengers 45

Relative change 21–22, 26–27, 83, 105, 292

Relative rate of change 27, 41, 83, 105–106, 125, 139, 145, 149–151, 155, 159, 164, 289, 291–293, 295–296

Rent control 283, 285

Resale value 31, 36

Revenue function 29, 35–36, 60, 67, 69, 83, 115, 120, 125, 140, 163, 192–194, 205–206, 224, 229, 263, 304, 350, 359

Sales forecasts 6, 106, 113, 211–212, 214, 288

Sales of books 42

Sales of CDs 14, 123, 212

Stock market 26–27, 45

Supply curve 31–34, 37–38, 61, 80, 280, 282–283, 285, 294, 296

Surplus 281

Taxes 33–34, 38, 59, 83

Tax cut or rebate 461, 463, 468

Tobacco production 24

Total cost 27, 35–36, 78, 73, 109, 118–120, 189–191, 193, 195–196, 198–201, 224–225, 229–230, 261–263, 266, 269, 277, 304, 351, 361, 381, 388, 394, 468

Total profit 36, 188, 192–194, 224–225, 378

Total revenue 29, 35–36, 78, 118, 151, 155, 189–191, 193–195, 206, 224–225, 263, 304, 378

Total utility 115

Value of a car 4

Variable cost 27, 35–37, 79, 195, 197, 262–263

Vehicles per person 50

Wage, real 195

Warehouse storage 195, 266, 279

Waste collection 14, 139, 259

Water supply charges 78

World production
    automobile 24
    beer 75, 370
    bicycle 23
    coal 256
    gold 122
    grain 14
    meat 108
    milk 13
    solar cell 105, 257
    solar power 145
    soybean 45, 105
    tobacco 24
    zinc 37

Yield, annual 297–298

Life Sciences and Ecology

Algae population growth 7, 279

AIDS 57, 292

Bacterial colony growth 81, 240–241, 253, 258, 293, 372

Bird flight 124, 187

Birds and worms 227, 432–434, 436

Birth and death rates 258, 290–293, 296

Blood pressure 188, 279, 363, 370–371, 459

Body mass of a mammal 64, 68, 150

Cancer rates 7, 79, 338

Carbon dioxide levels 269

Cardiac output 363, 370–371

Carrying capacity 111, 210, 214, 229, 313, 406

Clutch size 187

Competition 435–436

Cricket chirp patterns 3

Crows and whelks 186

Decomposition of leaves 443, 445

Deforestation 44

Density function 328–346

Dialysis, kidney 444

Dolphin speed 61

Drug concentrations 6, 40, 57, 63, 89, 97, 103, 145, 154, 161, 185, 187, 212–213, 215–223, 229, 255–256, 259–260, 269, 316, 318, 323, 345, 351–352, 361, 369–371, 405, 421–424, 430–431, 443–445, 454, 459, 463–467, 469

Drug saturation curve 63

Endocrinology 258

Energy (calorie) expenditure 68, 369, 443

Environmental Protection Agency (EPA) 51, 144, 267

Exponential growth and decay 39–41, 43–44, 49–53, 55, 57, 84, 295, 401, 417, 419, 449

Fever 114, 174

Firebreaks and forest fires 230–231, 258

Fish growth 25, 68, 107

Fish harvest 25, 335–337, 343, 404, 408, 444, 446–447

Fish population 50, 139, 145, 187, 239, 404, 408, 411, 444, 447

Foraging time 186

Fox population 392

Global warming 356

Gompertz growth equation 228, 417

Ground contamination 57, 77, 405

Growth of a tumor 94, 417, 443

Half–life and decay 52, 56–58, 81, 84, 216, 421–422, 443, 459, 464, 466–467, 469

Heartbeat patterns 3, 279

Heart rate 6, 15, 26, 109, 259

Hematocrit 187

HIV–AIDS 57, 292

Insect lifespan 331, 344

Insect population 407

Ion channel 216

Island species 57, 66, 68, 180

Kleiber's Law 82

Koala population 57, 207

Lizard loping 26

Loading curve (in feeding birds) 227

Logistic growth 111, 207–216, 222, 224–226, 229, 406, 446
Lotka–Volterra equations 432, 434
Lung 75, 79, 107, 158, 216
Money supply 375–376
Muscle contraction 25–26, 108
Nicotine 6, 25, 56, 108, 216, 220, 430, 459, 466
Photosynthesis 183, 185, 269, 320
Plant growth 183, 186, 254–255, 265, 269, 337–338
Pollutant levels 17, 81, 114, 265, 267, 394, 405, 407, 420, 422, 444
Population genetics 447
Predator–prey cycles 432–436
Pulmonologist 107
Rabbit population 180–181, 313
Rain forest 24, 109
Rats and formaldehyde 365–366, 370
Relative change 21–22, 26–27, 83, 105, 292
Relative rate of change 27, 41, 83, 105–106, 125, 139, 145, 149–151, 155, 159, 164, 289, 291–293, 295–296
Ricker curve 187
SARS 214, 448
Species density 362
Species diversity 6–7, 14, 66, 68, 76, 158
Sperm count 78
Spread of a disease 187, 209, 214, 437–441, 448, 454
Starvation 57, 109, 187, 258
Sturgeon length 25, 107
Sustainable yield 446
Symbiosis 432, 435
Toxicity 363, 365
Tree growth 122, 186, 258, 297, 331, 338
Urology 320
Vaccination 46, 437, 439
Waste generation 10, 259, 267, 394
Water flow 181, 268, 408, 420
Water pollution 81, 239, 267, 405, 420–422
Zebra mussel population 45, 139

Social Sciences

Abortion rate 112
Age distribution 328, 332–333
Ancestors 469
Baby boom 211
Birth and death rates 258, 290–293, 296
Commuting 370

Computer virus 214
Density function 328–346
Distribution of resources 115, 207, 295, 297, 464
DuBois formula 69
Ebbinghaus model for forgetting 431
Education trends 151, 331
GPAs 338
Happiness 361
Health care 328
Human body weight 15, 69, 107–108, 132, 257, 368–369, 395, 443
Human height prediction 258
Indifference curve 388–389
Infant mortality rates and health care 344
IQ scores 343
Land use 214, 423
Learning patterns 430
Monod growth curve 154
Normal distribution 161, 342–343, 346
Olympic records 8, 16–17, 41, 81
Okun's Law 13
Population density 362, 392
Population growth 5, 13, 21, 25, 39–41, 43–46, 48, 50–52, 56–58, 69, 82–83, 85, 94–95, 100, 110–111, 122, 125, 139, 142–143, 145–146, 154, 159, 162, 164, 177, 180–181, 187, 207–211, 213–214, 216, 226, 229, 237, 239–240, 253–256, 258, 263, 265, 277, 279, 289–293, 295–297, 312–313, 401, 404, 406–409, 411, 415, 419, 422–423, 432–436, 444, 446–448, 470
Population, United States 26, 85, 94–95, 162, 207–211, 214, 328, 332, 335, 340, 346
Population, world 24–25, 44, 94, 159, 164, 239, 312
Poverty line 114
Relative change 21–22, 26–27, 83, 105, 292
Relative rate of change 27, 41, 83, 105–106, 125, 139, 145, 149–151, 155, 159, 164, 289, 291–293, 295–296
Rituals 393
Scholarship funds 468
Search and rescue 14
Sports 470
Spread of a rumor 213

Test scores 343–344
Test success rates 339
Traffic patterns 100, 123, 132
Waiting times 219, 330–331, 337, 343, 346
Wave 70–72, 393
Wikipedia 56, 407
Winning probability 470
Zipf's Law 68, 140

Physical Sciences

Acceleration 104, 115, 123, 239, 256, 260, 268
Air pressure 57, 81, 163
Amplitude 70–76, 82, 84, 163
Ballooning 101, 260
Beam strength 67
Brightness of a star 76
Carbon–14 45, 160, 441, 442
Carbon dioxide concentration 5, 80, 269
Chemical reactions 106, 188, 422
Chlorofluorocarbons (CFCs) 5, 52
Daylight hours 158, 279
Density function 328–346
Distance 5, 13–14, 18, 20–21, 24, 26, 46, 65, 67, 77, 85, 93, 100, 102, 106, 121–122, 125–126, 132, 147, 151, 158, 160, 162, 164, 186–188, 207, 226–227, 229–230, 234–240, 254, 257, 260, 264–267, 291, 312, 339, 353, 362, 367, 369, 393–394, 397–399, 468
Elevation 6, 46, 83, 107, 122, 344–345, 355–356
Exponential growth and decay 39–41, 43–44, 49–53, 55, 57, 84, 295, 401, 417, 419, 449
Fog 353
Grand Canyon flooding 270
Gravitational force 67
Half–life and decay 52, 56–58, 81, 84, 216, 421–422, 443, 459, 464, 466–467, 469
Heat index 353, 358–359, 369
Height of a ball 140, 159, 265, 468
Height of a sand dune 24, 139
Isotherms 354
Illumination 126
Loudness 69
Missile range 380
Newtons laws of cooling and heating 161, 427–429, 431
Pendulum period 65, 140, 160
Radioactive decay 51, 57, 81, 146, 160, 260, 294, 407, 442–443

Relative change 21–22, 26–27, 83, 105, 292

Relative rate of change 27, 41, 83, 105–106, 125, 139, 145, 149–151, 155, 159, 164, 289, 291–293, 295–296

Specific heat 168

Temperature changes 2–4, 6–7, 46, 70–71, 74–78, 107, 114, 122–123, 125–126, 140, 145, 160–163, 174, 180, 185, 256, 276, 279–280, 353–354, 356–361, 367–370, 380, 389–392, 396, 406–407, 427–431, 441–442

Tide levels 74, 76, 158

Topographical maps 355, 360–361

Velocity, average 20–21, 24, 26, 67, 78, 83, 88–89, 93, 115, 121

Velocity, instantaneous 88–89, 93, 121

Velocity of a ball 140, 159, 265

Velocity of a bicycle 237, 265

Velocity of a car 7, 21, 122, 147, 234–235, 238–240, 254, 257, 265–268, 312, 343, 406, 441

Velocity of a mouse 267

Velocity of a particle 83, 93, 115, 121, 123, 259, 265

Velocity of a rocket 388

Velocity, vertical 158, 261

Velocity vs speed 20

Volcanic explosion 353

Volume of water 79, 179, 181, 220, 239–240, 269, 420

Volume of air in the lungs 75, 107, 158

Volume of a tank 1122, 258, 268

Weather map 354, 380

Wind chill 140, 389–390, 392

Wind energy 45, 56

Wind speed 122, 140, 389–390, 392

To Students: How to Learn from this Book

- This book may be different from other math textbooks that you have used, so it may be helpful to know about some of the differences in advance. At every stage, this book emphasizes the *meaning* (in practical, graphical or numerical terms) of the symbols you are using. There is much less emphasis on "plug-and-chug" and using formulas, and much more emphasis on the interpretation of these formulas than you may expect. You will often be asked to explain your ideas in words or to explain an answer using graphs.

- The book contains the main ideas of calculus in plain English. Success in using this book will depend on reading, questioning, and thinking hard about the ideas presented. It will be helpful to read the text in detail, not just the worked examples.

- There are few examples in the text that are exactly like the homework problems, so homework problems can't be done by searching for similar–looking "worked out" examples. Success with the homework will come by grappling with the ideas of calculus.

- For many problems in the book, there is more than one correct approach and more than one correct solution. Sometimes, solving a problem relies on common sense ideas that are not stated in the problem explicitly but which you know from everyday life.

- Some problems in this book assume that you have access to a graphing calculator or computer. There are many situations where you may not be able to find an exact solution to a problem, but you can use a calculator or computer to get a reasonable approximation.

- This book attempts to give equal weight to four methods for describing functions: graphical (a picture), numerical (a table of values), algebraic (a formula), and verbal (words). Sometimes it's easier to translate a problem given in one form into another. For example, you might replace the graph of a parabola with its equation, or plot a table of values to see its behavior. It is important to be flexible about your approach: if one way of looking at a problem doesn't work, try another.

- Students using this book have found discussing these problems in small groups helpful. There are a great many problems which are not cut-and-dried; it can help to attack them with the other perspectives your colleagues can provide. If group work is not feasible, see if your instructor can organize a discussion session in which additional problems can be worked on.

- You are probably wondering what you'll get from the book. The answer is, if you put in a solid effort, you will get a real understanding of one of the crowning achievements of human creativity—calculus—as well as a real sense of the power of mathematics in the age of technology.

CONTENTS

1 FUNCTIONS AND CHANGE   1

    1.1 WHAT IS A FUNCTION?   2

    1.2 LINEAR FUNCTIONS   8

    1.3 AVERAGE RATE OF CHANGE AND RELATIVE CHANGE   16

    1.4 APPLICATIONS OF FUNCTIONS TO ECONOMICS   27

    1.5 EXPONENTIAL FUNCTIONS   38

    1.6 THE NATURAL LOGARITHM   46

    1.7 EXPONENTIAL GROWTH AND DECAY   51

    1.8 NEW FUNCTIONS FROM OLD   59

    1.9 PROPORTIONALITY AND POWER FUNCTIONS   64

    1.10 PERIODIC FUNCTIONS   70

        REVIEW PROBLEMS   77

        CHECK YOUR UNDERSTANDING   82

    PROJECTS: COMPOUND INTEREST, POPULATION CENTER OF THE US   84

2 RATE OF CHANGE: THE DERIVATIVE   87

    2.1 INSTANTANEOUS RATE OF CHANGE   88

    2.2 THE DERIVATIVE FUNCTION   95

    2.3 INTERPRETATIONS OF THE DERIVATIVE   101

    2.4 THE SECOND DERIVATIVE   110

    2.5 MARGINAL COST AND REVENUE   115

        REVIEW PROBLEMS   121

        CHECK YOUR UNDERSTANDING   124

    PROJECTS: ESTIMATING TEMPERATURE OF A YAM, TEMPERATURE AND ILLUMINATION   125

FOCUS ON THEORY   127
    LIMITS, CONTINUITY, AND THE DEFINITION OF THE DERIVATIVE

3 SHORTCUTS TO DIFFERENTIATION   133

    3.1 DERIVATIVE FORMULAS FOR POWERS AND POLYNOMIALS   134

    3.2 EXPONENTIAL AND LOGARITHMIC FUNCTIONS   141

    3.3 THE CHAIN RULE   146

3.4 THE PRODUCT AND QUOTIENT RULES   151

3.5 DERIVATIVES OF PERIODIC FUNCTIONS   155

    REVIEW PROBLEMS   159

    CHECK YOUR UNDERSTANDING   162

PROJECTS: CORONER'S RULE OF THUMB; AIR PRESSURE AND ALTITUDE; RELATIVE GROWTH
RATES: POPULATION, GDP, AND GDP PER CAPITA   163

FOCUS ON THEORY   165
ESTABLISHING THE DERIVATIVE FORMULAS

FOCUS ON PRACTICE   168

4 USING THE DERIVATIVE   169

4.1 LOCAL MAXIMA AND MINIMA   170

4.2 INFLECTION POINTS   176

4.3 GLOBAL MAXIMA AND MINIMA   182

4.4 PROFIT, COST, AND REVENUE   188

4.5 AVERAGE COST   196

4.6 ELASTICITY OF DEMAND   202

4.7 LOGISTIC GROWTH   207

4.8 THE SURGE FUNCTION AND DRUG CONCENTRATION   216

    REVIEW PROBLEMS   222

    CHECK YOUR UNDERSTANDING   228

PROJECTS: AVERAGE AND MARGINAL COSTS, FIREBREAKS, PRODUCTION AND THE PRICE OF
RAW MATERIALS   230

5 ACCUMULATED CHANGE: THE DEFINITE INTEGRAL   233

5.1 DISTANCE AND ACCUMULATED CHANGE   234

5.2 THE DEFINITE INTEGRAL   240

5.3 THE DEFINITE INTEGRAL AS AREA   247

5.4 INTERPRETATIONS OF THE DEFINITE INTEGRAL   253

5.5 THE FUNDAMENTAL THEOREM OF CALCULUS   260

    REVIEW PROBLEMS   264

    CHECK YOUR UNDERSTANDING   267

PROJECTS: CARBON DIOXIDE IN POND WATER, FLOODING IN THE GRAND CANYON   269

FOCUS ON THEORY   271
THEOREMS ABOUT DEFINITE INTEGRALS

6 USING THE DEFINITE INTEGRAL   275

6.1 AVERAGE VALUE   276

6.2 CONSUMER AND PRODUCER SURPLUS   280

6.3 PRESENT AND FUTURE VALUE   286

6.4 INTEGRATING RELATIVE GROWTH RATES   289

REVIEW PROBLEMS   294

CHECK YOUR UNDERSTANDING   296

PROJECTS: DISTRIBUTION OF RESOURCES, YIELD FROM AN APPLE ORCHARD   297

7 ANTIDERIVATIVES   299

7.1 CONSTRUCTING ANTIDERIVATIVES ANALYTICALLY   300

7.2 INTEGRATION BY SUBSTITUTION   304

7.3 USING THE FUNDAMENTAL THEOREM TO FIND DEFINITE INTEGRALS   308

7.4 INTEGRATION BY PARTS   313

7.5 ANALYZING ANTIDERIVATIVES GRAPHICALLY AND NUMERICALLY   316

REVIEW PROBLEMS   322

CHECK YOUR UNDERSTANDING   324

PROJECTS: QUABBIN RESERVOIR   325

FOCUS ON PRACTICE   326

8 PROBABILITY   327

8.1 DENSITY FUNCTIONS   328

8.2 CUMULATIVE DISTRIBUTION FUNCTIONS AND PROBABILITY   332

8.3 THE MEDIAN AND THE MEAN   339

REVIEW PROBLEMS   344

CHECK YOUR UNDERSTANDING   346

PROJECTS: TRIANGULAR PROBABILITY DISTRIBUTION   346

9 FUNCTIONS OF SEVERAL VARIABLES   349

9.1 UNDERSTANDING FUNCTIONS OF TWO VARIABLES   350

9.2 CONTOUR DIAGRAMS   354

9.3 PARTIAL DERIVATIVES   364

9.4 COMPUTING PARTIAL DERIVATIVES ALGEBRAICALLY   371

9.5 CRITICAL POINTS AND OPTIMIZATION   376

9.6 CONSTRAINED OPTIMIZATION   381

REVIEW PROBLEMS   389

CHECK YOUR UNDERSTANDING   394

PROJECTS: A HEATER IN A ROOM, OPTIMIZING RELATIVE PRICES FOR ADULTS AND CHIL-DREN, MAXIMIZING PRODUCTION AND MINIMIZING COST: "DUALITY"   396

FOCUS ON THEORY   397

DERIVING THE FORMULA FOR A REGRESSION LINE

10 MATHEMATICAL MODELING USING DIFFERENTIAL EQUATIONS   403

10.1 MATHEMATICAL MODELING: SETTING UP A DIFFERENTIAL EQUATION   404

10.2 SOLUTIONS OF DIFFERENTIAL EQUATIONS   408

10.3 SLOPE FIELDS   412

10.4 EXPONENTIAL GROWTH AND DECAY   417

10.5 APPLICATIONS AND MODELING   423

10.6 MODELING THE INTERACTION OF TWO POPULATIONS   432

10.7 MODELING THE SPREAD OF A DISEASE   437

REVIEW PROBLEMS   441

CHECK YOUR UNDERSTANDING   444

PROJECTS: HARVESTING AND LOGISTIC GROWTH, POPULATION GENETICS, THE SPREAD OF SARS   446

FOCUS ON THEORY   449

SEPARATION OF VARIABLES

11 GEOMETRIC SERIES   453

11.1 GEOMETRIC SERIES   454

11.2 APPLICATIONS TO BUSINESS AND ECONOMICS   459

11.3 APPLICATIONS TO THE NATURAL SCIENCES   463

REVIEW PROBLEMS   467

CHECK YOUR UNDERSTANDING   468

PROJECTS: DO YOU HAVE ANY COMMON ANCESTORS?, HARROD-HICKS MODEL OF AN EX-PANDING NATIONAL ECONOMY, PROBABILITY OF WINNING IN SPORTS   469

APPENDICES   471

A FITTING FORMULAS TO DATA   472

B COMPOUND INTEREST AND THE NUMBER *e*   480

C SPREADSHEET PROJECTS   485

   1. MALTHUS: POPULATION OUTSTRIPS FOOD SUPPLY   485

   2. CREDIT CARD DEBT   486

   3. CHOOSING A BANK LOAN   487

   4. COMPARING HOME MORTGAGES   488

   5. PRESENT VALUE OF LOTTERY WINNINGS   489

   6. COMPARING INVESTMENTS   489

   7. INVESTING FOR THE FUTURE: TUITION PAYMENTS   490

   8. NEW OR USED?   490

   9. VERHULST: THE LOGISTIC MODEL   491

   10. THE SPREAD OF INFORMATION: A COMPARISON OF TWO MODELS   492

   11. THE FLU IN WORLD WAR I   492

ANSWERS TO ODD-NUMBERED PROBLEMS   495

PRETEST   521

INDEX   525

Chapter One

FUNCTIONS AND CHANGE

Contents

1.1 **What is a Function?** **2**

    The Rule of Four 2

    Mathematical Modeling 3

    Function Notation and Intercepts 4

    Increasing and Decreasing Functions 4

1.2 **Linear Functions** **8**

    Families of Linear Functions 12

1.3 **Average Rate of Change and Relative Change** **16**

    Visualizing Rate of Change 18

    Concavity 19

    Distance, Velocity, and Speed 20

    Relative Change 21

1.4 **Applications of Functions to Economics** . . . **27**

    Cost, Revenue, and Profit Functions 27

    Marginal Cost, Revenue, and Profit 31

    Supply and Demand Curves 31

    A Budget Constraint 34

1.5 **Exponential Functions** **38**

    Population Growth 39

    Elimination of a Drug from the Body 40

    The General Exponential Function 41

1.6 **The Natural Logarithm** **46**

    Solving Equations Using Logarithms 47

    Exponential Functions with Base e 48

1.7 **Exponential Growth and Decay** **51**

    Doubling Time and Half-Life 52

    Financial Applications: Compound Interest . 53

1.8 **New Functions from Old** **59**

    Composite Functions 59

    Stretches of Graphs 60

    Shifted Graphs 60

1.9 **Proportionality and Power Functions** **64**

    Proportionality 64

    Power Functions 65

    Quadratic Functions and Polynomials 66

1.10 **Periodic Functions** **70**

    The Sine and Cosine 71

    REVIEW PROBLEMS **77**

    CHECK YOUR UNDERSTANDING **82**

PROJECTS: Compound Interest, Population Center of the US **84**

1.1 WHAT IS A FUNCTION?

In mathematics, a *function* is used to represent the dependence of one quantity upon another.

Let's look at an example. In December 2008, International Falls, Minnesota, was very cold over winter vacation. The daily low temperatures for December 17–26 are given in Table 1.1.[1]

Table 1.1 *Daily low temperature in International Falls, Minnesota, December 17–26, 2008*

Date	17	18	19	20	21	22	23	24	25	26
Low temperature (°F)	−14	−15	−12	−4	−15	−18	1	−9	−10	16

Although you may not have thought of something so unpredictable as temperature as being a function, the temperature *is* a function of date, because each day gives rise to one and only one low temperature. There is no formula for temperature (otherwise we would not need the weather bureau), but nevertheless the temperature does satisfy the definition of a function: Each date, t, has a unique low temperature, L, associated with it.

We define a function as follows:

> A **function** is a rule that takes certain numbers as inputs and assigns to each a definite output number. The set of all input numbers is called the **domain** of the function and the set of resulting output numbers is called the **range** of the function.

The input is called the *independent variable* and the output is called the *dependent variable*. In the temperature example, the set of dates $\{17, 18, 19, 20, 21, 22, 23, 24, 25, 26\}$ is the domain and the set of temperatures $\{-18, -15, -14, -12, -10, -9, -4, 1, 16\}$ is the range. We call the function f and write $L = f(t)$. Notice that a function may have identical outputs for different inputs (December 18 and 21, for example).

Some quantities, such as date, are *discrete*, meaning they take only certain isolated values (dates must be integers). Other quantities, such as time, are *continuous* as they can be any number. For a continuous variable, domains and ranges are often written using interval notation:

The set of numbers t such that $a \leq t \leq b$ is written $[a, b]$.

The set of numbers t such that $a < t < b$ is written (a, b).

The Rule of Four: Tables, Graphs, Formulas, and Words

Functions can be represented by tables, graphs, formulas, and descriptions in words. For example, the function giving the daily low temperatures in International Falls can be represented by the graph in Figure 1.1, as well as by Table 1.1.

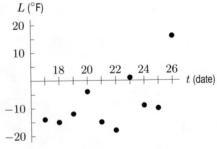

Figure 1.1: Daily low temperatures, International Falls, December 2008

[1] www.wunderground.com.

Other functions arise naturally as graphs. Figure 1.2 contains electrocardiogram (EKG) pictures showing the heartbeat patterns of two patients, one normal and one not. Although it is possible to construct a formula to approximate an EKG function, this is seldom done. The pattern of repetitions is what a doctor needs to know, and these are more easily seen from a graph than from a formula. However, each EKG gives electrical activity as a function of time.

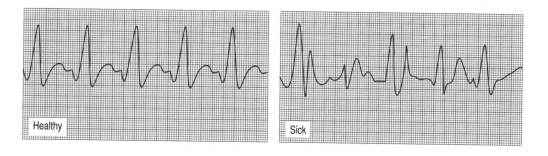

Figure 1.2: EKG readings on two patients

Consider the snow tree cricket. Surprisingly enough, all such crickets chirp at essentially the same rate if they are at the same temperature. That means that the chirp rate is a function of temperature. In other words, if we know the temperature, we can determine the chirp rate. Even more surprisingly, the chirp rate, C, in chirps per minute, increases steadily with the temperature, T, in degrees Fahrenheit, and can be computed, to a fair degree of accuracy, using the formula

$$C = f(T) = 4T - 160.$$

The graph of this function is in Figure 1.3.

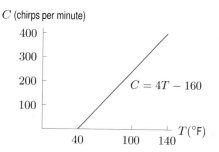

Figure 1.3: Cricket chirp rate as a function of temperature

Mathematical Modeling

A *mathematical model* is a mathematical description of a real situation. In this book we consider models that are functions.

Modeling almost always involves some simplification of reality. We choose which variables to include and which to ignore—for example, we consider the dependence of chirp rate on temperature, but not on other variables. The choice of variables is based on knowledge of the context (the biology of crickets, for example), not on mathematics. To test the model, we compare its predictions with observations.

In this book, we often model a situation that has a discrete domain with a continuous function whose domain is an interval of numbers. For example, the annual US gross domestic product (GDP) has a value for each year, $t = 0, 1, 2, 3, \ldots$ etc. We may model it by a function of the form $G = f(t)$, with values for t in a continuous interval. In doing this, we expect that the values of $f(t)$ match the values of the GDP at the points $t = 0, 1, 2, 3, \ldots$ etc., and that information obtained from $f(t)$ closely matches observed values.

Used judiciously, a mathematical model captures trends in the data to enable us to analyze and make predictions. A common way of finding a model is described in Appendix A.

Function Notation and Intercepts

We write $y = f(t)$ to express the fact that y is a function of t. The independent variable is t, the dependent variable is y, and f is the name of the function. The graph of a function has an *intercept* where it crosses the horizontal or vertical axis. Horizontal intercepts are also called the *zeros* of the function.

Example 1   The value of a car, V, is a function of the age of the car, a, so $V = g(a)$, where g is the name we are giving to this function.

(a) Interpret the statement $g(5) = 9$ in terms of the value of a car if V is in thousands of dollars and a is in years.
(b) In the same units, the value of a Honda[2] is approximated by $g(a) = 13.78 - 0.8a$. Find and interpret the vertical and horizontal intercepts of the graph of this depreciation function g.

Solution   (a) Since $V = g(a)$, the statement $g(5) = 9$ means $V = 9$ when $a = 5$. This tells us that the car is worth $9000 when it is 5 years old.
(b) Since $V = g(a)$, a graph of the function g has the value of the car on the vertical axis and the age of the car on the horizontal axis. The vertical intercept is the value of V when $a = 0$. It is $V = g(0) = 13.78$, so the Honda was valued at $13,780 when new. The horizontal intercept is the value of a such that $g(a) = 0$, so

$$13.78 - 0.8a = 0$$
$$a = \frac{13.78}{0.8} = 17.2.$$

At age 17 years, the Honda has no value.

Increasing and Decreasing Functions

In the previous examples, the chirp rate increases with temperature, while the value of the Honda decreases with age. We express these facts saying that f is an increasing function, while g is decreasing. In general:

> A function f is **increasing** if the values of $f(x)$ increase as x increases.
> A function f is **decreasing** if the values of $f(x)$ decrease as x increases.
>
> The graph of an *increasing* function *climbs* as we move from left to right.
> The graph of a *decreasing* function *descends* as we move from left to right.

Figure 1.4: Increasing and decreasing functions

[2]From data obtained from the Kelley Blue Book, www.kbb.com.

Problems for Section 1.1

1. Which graph in Figure 1.5 best matches each of the following stories?[3] Write a story for the remaining graph.

  (a) I had just left home when I realized I had forgotten my books, and so I went back to pick them up.
  (b) Things went fine until I had a flat tire.
  (c) I started out calmly but sped up when I realized I was going to be late.

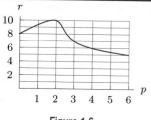

Figure 1.6

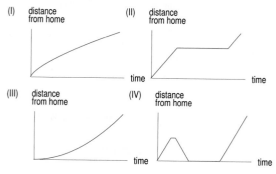

Figure 1.5

2. The population of a city, P, in millions, is a function of t, the number of years since 1970, so $P = f(t)$. Explain the meaning of the statement $f(35) = 12$ in terms of the population of this city.

3. Let $W = f(t)$ represent wheat production in Argentina,[4] in millions of metric tons, where t is years since 1990. Interpret the statement $f(12) = 9$ in terms of wheat production.

4. The concentration of carbon dioxide, $C = f(t)$, in the atmosphere, in parts per million (ppm), is a function of years, t, since 1960.

  (a) Interpret $f(40) = 370$ in terms of carbon dioxide.[5]
  (b) What is the meaning of $f(50)$?

5. The population of Washington DC grew from 1900 to 1950, stayed approximately constant during the 1950s, and decreased from about 1960 to 2005. Graph the population as a function of years since 1900.

6. (a) The graph of $r = f(p)$ is in Figure 1.6. What is the value of r when p is 0? When p is 3?
  (b) What is $f(2)$?

For the functions in Problems 7–11, find $f(5)$.

7. $f(x) = 2x + 3$ **8.** $f(x) = 10x - x^2$

9.

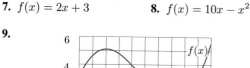

10.

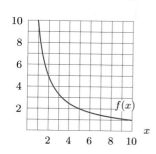

11.

x	1	2	3	4	5	6	7	8
$f(x)$	2.3	2.8	3.2	3.7	4.1	5.0	5.6	6.2

12. Let $y = f(x) = x^2 + 2$.
  (a) Find the value of y when x is zero.
  (b) What is $f(3)$?
  (c) What values of x give y a value of 11?
  (d) Are there any values of x that give y a value of 1?

13. The use of CFCs (chlorofluorocarbons) has declined since the 1987 Montreal Protocol came into force to reduce the use of substances that deplete the ozone layer. World annual CFC consumption, $C = f(t)$, in million tons, is a function of time, t, in years since 1987. (CFCs are measured by the weight of ozone that they could destroy.)

  (a) Interpret $f(10) = 0.2$ in terms of CFCs.[6]

---

[3] Adapted from Jan Terwel, "Real Math in Cooperative Groups in Secondary Education." *Cooperative Learning in Mathematics*, ed. Neal Davidson, p. 234 (Reading: Addison Wesley, 1990).
[4] www.usda.gov.oce/weather/pubs/Other/MWCACP/Graphs/Argentina/ArgentinaWheat.pdf.
[5] *Vital Signs 2007-2008*, The Worldwatch Institute, W.W. Norton & Company, 2007, p. 43.
[6] *Vital Signs 2007-2008*, The Worldwatch Institute, W.W. Norton & Company, 2007, p. 47.

(b) Interpret the vertical intercept of the graph of this function in terms of CFCs.

(c) Interpret the horizontal intercept of the graph of this function in terms of CFCs.

14. Figure 1.7 shows the amount of nicotine, $N = f(t)$, in mg, in a person's bloodstream as a function of the time, t, in hours, since the person finished smoking a cigarette.

(a) Estimate $f(3)$ and interpret it in terms of nicotine.

(b) About how many hours have passed before the nicotine level is down to 0.1 mg?

(c) What is the vertical intercept? What does it represent in terms of nicotine?

(d) If this function had a horizontal intercept, what would it represent?

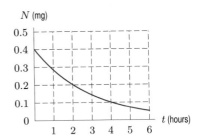

Figure 1.7

15. The number of sales per month, S, is a function of the amount, a (in dollars), spent on advertising that month, so $S = f(a)$.

(a) Interpret the statement $f(1000) = 3500$.

(b) Which of the graphs in Figure 1.8 is more likely to represent this function?

(c) What does the vertical intercept of the graph of this function represent, in terms of sales and advertising?

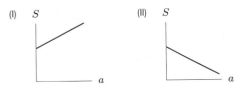

Figure 1.8

16. A deposit is made into an interest-bearing account. Figure 1.9 shows the balance, B, in the account t years later.

(a) What was the original deposit?

(b) Estimate $f(10)$ and interpret it.

(c) When does the balance reach $5000?

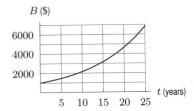

Figure 1.9

17. When a patient with a rapid heart rate takes a drug, the heart rate plunges dramatically and then slowly rises again as the drug wears off. Sketch the heart rate against time from the moment the drug is administered.

18. In the Andes mountains in Peru, the number, N, of species of bats is a function of the elevation, h, in feet above sea level, so $N = f(h)$.

(a) Interpret the statement $f(500) = 100$ in terms of bat species.

(b) What are the meanings of the vertical intercept, k, and horizontal intercept, c, in Figure 1.10?

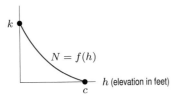

Figure 1.10

19. After an injection, the concentration of a drug in a patient's body increases rapidly to a peak and then slowly decreases. Graph the concentration of the drug in the body as a function of the time since the injection was given. Assume that the patient has none of the drug in the body before the injection. Label the peak concentration and the time it takes to reach that concentration.

20. An object is put outside on a cold day at time $t = 0$. Its temperature, $H = f(t)$, in °C, is graphed in Figure 1.11.

(a) What does the statement $f(30) = 10$ mean in terms of temperature? Include units for 30 and for 10 in your answer.

(b) Explain what the vertical intercept, a, and the horizontal intercept, b, represent in terms of temperature of the object and time outside.

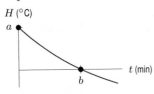

Figure 1.11

21. Financial investors know that, in general, the higher the expected rate of return on an investment, the higher the corresponding risk.

(a) Graph this relationship, showing expected return as a function of risk.

(b) On the figure from part (a), mark a point with high expected return and low risk. (Investors hope to find such opportunities.)

22. In tide pools on the New England coast, snails eat algae. Describe what Figure 1.12 tells you about the effect of snails on the diversity of algae.[7] Does the graph support the statement that diversity peaks at intermediate predation levels?

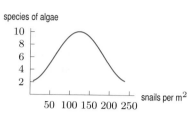

species of algae

snails per m^2

Figure 1.12

23. **(a)** A potato is put in an oven to bake at time $t = 0$. Which of the graphs in Figure 1.13 could represent the potato's temperature as a function of time?
(b) What does the vertical intercept represent in terms of the potato's temperature?

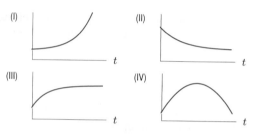

Figure 1.13

24. Figure 1.14 shows fifty years of fertilizer use in the US, India, and the former Soviet Union.[8]

(a) Estimate fertilizer use in 1970 in the US, India, and the former Soviet Union.
(b) Write a sentence for each of the three graphs describing how fertilizer use has changed in each region over this 50-year period.

Figure 1.14

25. The gas mileage of a car (in miles per gallon) is highest when the car is going about 45 miles per hour and is lower when the car is going faster or slower than 45 mph. Graph gas mileage as a function of speed of the car.

26. The six graphs in Figure 1.15 show frequently observed patterns of age-specific cancer incidence rates, in number of cases per 1000 people, as a function of age.[9] The scales on the vertical axes are equal.

(a) For each of the six graphs, write a sentence explaining the effect of age on the cancer rate.
(b) Which graph shows a relatively high incidence rate for children? Suggest a type of cancer that behaves this way.
(c) Which graph shows a brief decrease in the incidence rate at around age 50? Suggest a type of cancer that might behave this way.
(d) Which graph or graphs might represent a cancer that is caused by toxins which build up in the body over time? (For example, lung cancer.) Explain.

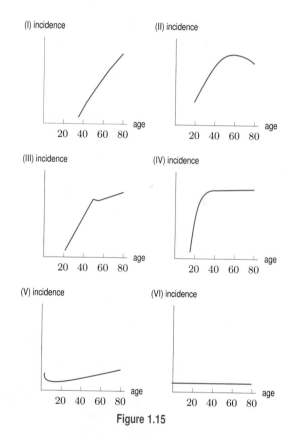

Figure 1.15

[7]Rosenzweig, M.L., *Species Diversity in Space and Time,* p. 343 (Cambridge: Cambridge University Press, 1995).
[8]The Worldwatch Institute, *Vital Signs 2001,* p. 32 (New York: W.W. Norton, 2001).
[9]Abraham M. Lilienfeld, *Foundations of Epidemiology,* p. 155 (New York: Oxford University Press, 1976).

1.2   LINEAR FUNCTIONS

Probably the most commonly used functions are the *linear functions*, whose graphs are straight lines. The chirp-rate and the Honda depreciation functions in the previous section are both linear. We now look at more examples of linear functions.

Olympic and World Records

During the early years of the Olympics, the height of the men's winning pole vault increased approximately 8 inches every four years. Table 1.2 shows that the height started at 130 inches in 1900, and increased by the equivalent of 2 inches a year between 1900 and 1912. So the height was a linear function of time.

Table 1.2   *Winning height (approximate) for Men's Olympic pole vault*

Year	1900	1904	1908	1912
Height (inches)	130	138	146	154

If y is the winning height in inches and t is the number of years since 1900, we can write

$$y = f(t) = 130 + 2t.$$

Since $y = f(t)$ increases with t, we see that f is an increasing function. The coefficient 2 tells us the rate, in inches per year, at which the height increases. This rate is the *slope* of the line in Figure 1.16. The slope is given by the ratio

$$\text{Slope} = \frac{\text{Rise}}{\text{Run}} = \frac{146 - 138}{8 - 4} = \frac{8}{4} = 2 \text{ inches/year.}$$

Calculating the slope (rise/run) using any other two points on the line gives the same value.

What about the constant 130? This represents the initial height in 1900, when $t = 0$. Geometrically, 130 is the intercept on the vertical axis.

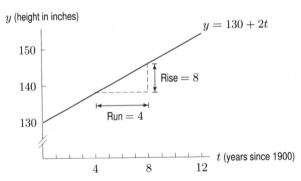

Figure 1.16: Olympic pole vault records

You may wonder whether the linear trend continues beyond 1912. Not surprisingly, it does not exactly. The formula $y = 130 + 2t$ predicts that the height in the 2008 Olympics would be 346 inches or 28 feet 10 inches, which is considerably higher than the actual value of 19 feet 4.25 inches.[10] There is clearly a danger in *extrapolating* too far from the given data. You should also observe that the data in Table 1.2 is *discrete*, because it is given only at specific points (every four years). However, we have treated the variable t as though it were *continuous*, because the function $y = 130 + 2t$ makes sense for all values of t. The graph in Figure 1.16 is of the continuous function because it is a solid line, rather than four separate points representing the years in which the Olympics were held.

---

[10]http://sports.espn.go.com/olympics/summer08.

Example 1   If y is the world record time to run the mile, in seconds, and t is the number of years since 1900, then records show that, approximately,

$$y = g(t) = 260 - 0.4t.$$

Explain the meaning of the intercept, 260, and the slope, -0.4, in terms of the world record time to run the mile and sketch the graph.

Solution   The intercept, 260, tells us that the world record was 260 seconds in 1900 (at $t = 0$). The slope, -0.4, tells us that the world record decreased at a rate of about 0.4 seconds per year. See Figure 1.17.

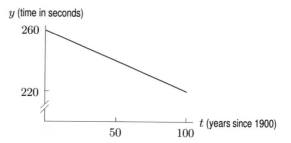

Figure 1.17: World record time to run the mile

Slope and Rate of Change

We use the symbol Δ (the Greek letter capital delta) to mean "change in," so Δx means change in x and Δy means change in y.

The slope of a linear function $y = f(x)$ can be calculated from values of the function at two points, given by x_1 and x_2, using the formula

$$\text{Slope} = \frac{\text{Rise}}{\text{Run}} = \frac{\Delta y}{\Delta x} = \frac{f(x_2) - f(x_1)}{x_2 - x_1}.$$

The quantity $(f(x_2) - f(x_1))/(x_2 - x_1)$ is called a *difference quotient* because it is the quotient of two differences. (See Figure 1.18.) Since slope $= \Delta y/\Delta x$, the slope represents the *rate of change* of y with respect to x. The units of the slope are y-units over x-units.

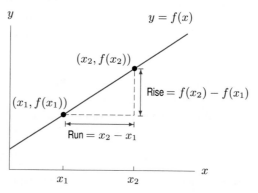

Figure 1.18: Difference quotient $= \dfrac{f(x_2) - f(x_1)}{x_2 - x_1}$

Linear Functions in General

> **A linear function** has the form
>
> $$y = f(x) = b + mx.$$
>
> Its graph is a line such that
> - m is the **slope**, or rate of change of y with respect to x.
> - b is the **vertical intercept** or value of y when x is zero.

If the slope, m, is positive, then f is an increasing function. If m is negative, then f is decreasing.
Notice that if the slope, m, is zero, we have $y = b$, a horizontal line. For a line of slope m through the point (x_0, y_0), we have

$$\text{Slope} = m = \frac{y - y_0}{x - x_0}.$$

Therefore we can write the equation of the line in the *point-slope form*:

> The equation of a line of slope m through the point (x_0, y_0) is
>
> $$y - y_0 = m(x - x_0).$$

Example 2   The solid waste generated each year in the cities of the US is increasing. The solid waste generated,[11] in millions of tons, was 238.3 in 2000 and 251.3 in 2006.

(a) Assuming that the amount of solid waste generated by US cities is a linear function of time, find a formula for this function by finding the equation of the line through these two points.
(b) Use this formula to predict the amount of solid waste generated in the year 2020.

Solution   (a) We think of the amount of solid waste, W, as a function of year, t, and the two points are $(2000, 238.3)$ and $(2006, 251.3)$. The slope of the line is

$$m = \frac{\Delta W}{\Delta t} = \frac{251.3 - 238.3}{2006 - 2000} = \frac{13}{6} = 2.167 \text{ million tons/year.}$$

We use the point-slope form to find the equation of the line. We substitute the point $(2000, 238.3)$ and the slope $m = 2.167$ into the equation:

$$W - W_0 = m(t - t_0)$$
$$W - 238.3 = 2.167(t - 2000)$$
$$W - 238.3 = 2.167t - 4334$$
$$W = 2.167t - 4095.7.$$

The equation of the line is $W = 2.167t - 4095.7$. Alternatively, we could use the slope-intercept form of a line to find the vertical intercept.

(b) To calculate solid waste predicted for the year 2020, we substitute $t = 2020$ into the equation of the line, $W = -4095.7 + 2.167t$, and calculate W:

$$W = -4095.7 + 2.167(2020) = 281.64.$$

The formula predicts that in the year 2020, there will be 281.64 million tons of solid waste.

---

[11] *Statistical Abstracts of the US*, 2009, Table 361.

> **Recognizing Data from a Linear Function:** Values of x and y in a table could come from a linear function $y = b + mx$ if differences in y-values are constant for equal differences in x.

Example 3 Which of the following tables of values could represent a linear function?

x	0	1	2	3
$f(x)$	25	30	35	40

x	0	2	4	6
$g(x)$	10	16	26	40

t	20	30	40	50
$h(t)$	2.4	2.2	2.0	1.8

Solution Since $f(x)$ increases by 5 for every increase of 1 in x, the values of $f(x)$ could be from a linear function with slope $= 5/1 = 5$.

Between $x = 0$ and $x = 2$, the value of $g(x)$ increases by 6 as x increases by 2. Between $x = 2$ and $x = 4$, the value of y increases by 10 as x increases by 2. Since the slope is not constant, $g(x)$ could not be a linear function.

Since $h(t)$ decreases by 0.2 for every increase of 10 in t, the values of $h(t)$ could be from a linear function with slope $= -0.2/10 = -0.02$.

Example 4 The data in the following table lie on a line. Find formulas for each of the following functions, and give units for the slope in each case:

(a) q as a function of p

(b) p as a function of q

p(dollars)	5	10	15	20
q(tons)	100	90	80	70

Solution (a) If we think of q as a linear function of p, then q is the dependent variable and p is the independent variable. We can use any two points to find the slope. The first two points give

$$\text{Slope} = m = \frac{\Delta q}{\Delta p} = \frac{90 - 100}{10 - 5} = \frac{-10}{5} = -2.$$

The units are the units of q over the units of p, or tons per dollar.

To write q as a linear function of p, we use the equation $q = b + mp$. We know that $m = -2$, and we can use any of the points in the table to find b. Substituting $p = 10$, $q = 90$ gives

$$q = b + mp$$
$$90 = b + (-2)(10)$$
$$90 = b - 20$$
$$110 = b.$$

Thus, the equation of the line is
$$q = 110 - 2p.$$

(b) If we now consider p as a linear function of q, then p is the dependent variable and q is the independent variable. We have

$$\text{Slope} = m = \frac{\Delta p}{\Delta q} = \frac{10 - 5}{90 - 100} = \frac{5}{-10} = -0.5.$$

The units of the slope are dollars per ton.

Since p is a linear function of q, we have $p = b + mq$ and $m = -0.5$. To find b, we substitute any point from the table, such as $p = 10$, $q = 90$, into this equation:

$$p = b + mq$$
$$10 = b + (-0.5)(90)$$
$$10 = b - 45$$
$$55 = b.$$

Thus, the equation of the line is

$$p = 55 - 0.5q.$$

Alternatively, we could take our answer to part (a), that is $q = 110 - 2p$, and solve for p. Appendix A shows how to fit a linear function to data that is not exactly linear.

Families of Linear Functions

Formulas such as $f(x) = b + mx$, in which the constants m and b can take on various values, represent a *family of functions*. All the functions in a family share certain properties—in this case, the graphs are lines. The constants m and b are called *parameters*. Figures 1.19 and 1.20 show graphs with several values of m and b. Notice the greater the magnitude of m, the steeper the line.

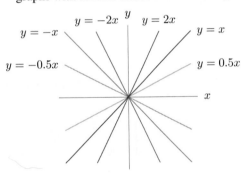

Figure 1.19: The family $y = mx$ (with $b = 0$)

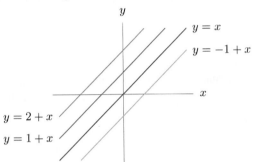

Figure 1.20: The family $y = b + x$ (with $m = 1$)

Problems for Section 1.2

For Problems 1–4, determine the slope and the y-intercept of the line whose equation is given.

1. $7y + 12x - 2 = 0$
2. $3x + 2y = 8$
3. $12x = 6y + 4$
4. $-4y + 2x + 8 = 0$

For Problems 5–8, find an equation for the line that passes through the given points.

5. $(0, 2)$ and $(2, 3)$
6. $(0, 0)$ and $(1, 1)$
7. $(-2, 1)$ and $(2, 3)$
8. $(4, 5)$ and $(2, -1)$

9. Figure 1.21 shows four lines given by equation $y = b + mx$. Match the lines to the conditions on the parameters m and b.

   (a) $m > 0, b > 0$ (b) $m < 0, b > 0$
   (c) $m > 0, b < 0$ (d) $m < 0, b < 0$

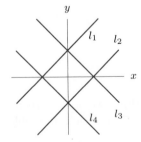

Figure 1.21

10. (a) Which two lines in Figure 1.22 have the same slope? Of these two lines, which has the larger y-intercept?
   (b) Which two lines have the same y-intercept? Of these two lines, which has the larger slope?

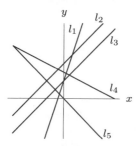

Figure 1.22

11. A city's population was 30,700 in the year 2000 and is growing by 850 people a year.

   (a) Give a formula for the city's population, P, as a function of the number of years, t, since 2000.
   (b) What is the population predicted to be in 2010?
   (c) When is the population expected to reach 45,000?

12. A cell phone company charges a monthly fee of $25 plus $0.05 per minute. Find a formula for the monthly charge, C, in dollars, as a function of the number of minutes, m, the phone is used during the month.

13. A company rents cars at $40 a day and 15 cents a mile. Its competitor's cars are $50 a day and 10 cents a mile.

   (a) For each company, give a formula for the cost of renting a car for a day as a function of the distance traveled.
   (b) On the same axes, graph both functions.
   (c) How should you decide which company is cheaper?

14. World milk production rose at an approximately constant rate between 1997 and 2003.[12] See Figure 1.23.

   (a) Estimate the vertical intercept and interpret it in terms of milk production.
   (b) Estimate the slope and interpret it in terms of milk production.
   (c) Give an approximate formula for milk production, M, as a function of t.

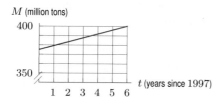

Figure 1.23

15. Annual revenue R from McDonald's restaurants worldwide can be estimated by $R = 19.1 + 1.8t$, where R is in billion dollars and t is in years since January 1, 2005.[13]

   (a) What is the slope of this function? Include units. Interpret the slope in terms of McDonald's revenue.
   (b) What is the vertical intercept of this function? Include units. Interpret the vertical intercept in terms of McDonald's revenue.
   (c) What annual revenue does the function predict for 2010?
   (d) When is annual revenue predicted to hit 30 billion dollars?

16. Let y be the percent increase in annual US national production during a year when the unemployment rate changes by u percent. (For example, $u = 2$ if unemployment increases from 4% to 6%.) Okun's law states that

$$y = 3.5 - 2u.$$

   (a) What is the meaning of the number 3.5 in Okun's law?
   (b) What is the effect on national production of a year when unemployment rises from 5% to 8%?
   (c) What change in the unemployment rate corresponds to a year when production is the same as the year before?
   (d) What is the meaning of the coefficient -2 in Okun's law?

17. Which of the following tables could represent linear functions?

   (a)

x	0	1	2	3
y	27	25	23	21

   (b)

t	15	20	25	30
s	62	72	82	92

   (c)

u	1	2	3	4
w	5	10	18	28

18. For each table in Problem 17 that could represent a linear function, find a formula for that function.

19. A company's pricing schedule in Table 1.3 is designed to encourage large orders. (A gross is 12 dozen.) Find a formula for:

   (a) q as a linear function of p.
   (b) p as a linear function of q.

Table 1.3

q (order size, gross)	3	4	5	6
p (price/dozen)	15	12	9	6

---

[12] *Statistical Abstracts of the US 2004–2005*, Table 1355.
[13] Based on McDonald's Annual Report 2007, accessed at www.mcdonalds.com.

20. Figure 1.24 shows the distance from home, in miles, of a person on a 5-hour trip.

    (a) Estimate the vertical intercept. Give units and interpret it in terms of distance from home.

    (b) Estimate the slope of this linear function. Give units, and interpret it in terms of distance from home.

    (c) Give a formula for distance, D, from home as a function of time, t in hours.

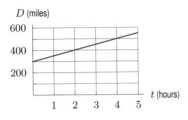

Figure 1.24

21. The percentage of people, P, below the poverty level in the US[14] is given in Table 1.4.

    (a) Find a formula for the percentage in poverty as a linear function of time in years since 2000.

    (b) Use the formula to predict the percentage in poverty in 2006.

    (c) What is the difference between the prediction and the actual percentage, 12.3%?

Table 1.4

Year (since 2000)	0	1	2	3
P (percentage)	11.3	11.7	12.1	12.5

22. World grain production was 1241 million tons in 1975 and 2048 million tons in 2005, and has been increasing at an approximately constant rate.[15]

    (a) Find a linear function for world grain production, P, in million tons, as a function of t, the number of years since 1975.

    (b) Using units, interpret the slope in terms of grain production.

    (c) Using units, interpret the vertical intercept in terms of grain production.

    (d) According to the linear model, what is the predicted world grain production in 2015?

    (e) According to the linear model, when is grain production predicted to reach 2500 million tons?

23. Search and rescue teams work to find lost hikers. Members of the search team separate and walk parallel to one another through the area to be searched. Table 1.5 shows the percent, P, of lost individuals found for various separation distances, d, of the searchers.[16]

Table 1.5

Separation distance d (ft)	20	40	60	80	100
Approximate percent found, P	90	80	70	60	50

    (a) Explain how you know that the percent found, P, could be a linear function of separation distance, d.

    (b) Find P as a linear function of d.

    (c) What is the slope of the function? Give units and interpret the answer.

    (d) What are the vertical and horizontal intercepts of the function? Give units and interpret the answers.

24. Annual sales of music compact discs (CDs) have declined since 2000. Sales were 942.5 million in 2000 and 384.7 million in 2008.[17]

    (a) Find a formula for annual sales, S, in millions of music CDs, as a linear function of the number of years, t, since 2000.

    (b) Give units for and interpret the slope and the vertical intercept of this function.

    (c) Use the formula to predict music CD sales in 2012.

25. In a California town, the monthly charge for waste collection is $8 for 32 gallons of waste and $12.32 for 68 gallons of waste.

    (a) Find a linear formula for the cost, C, of waste collection as a function of the number of gallons of waste, w.

    (b) What is the slope of the line found in part (a)? Give units and interpret your answer in terms of the cost of waste collection.

    (c) What is the vertical intercept of the line found in part (a)? Give units and interpret your answer in terms of the cost of waste collection.

26. The number of species of coastal dune plants in Australia decreases as the latitude, in °S, increases. There are 34 species at 11°S and 26 species at 44°S.[18]

    (a) Find a formula for the number, N, of species of coastal dune plants in Australia as a linear function of the latitude, l, in °S.

    (b) Give units for and interpret the slope and the vertical intercept of this function.

    (c) Graph this function between $l = 11°S$ and $l = 44°S$. (Australia lies entirely within these latitudes.)

[14] www.census.gov/hhes/www/poverty/histpov/hstpov2.html

[15] *Vital Signs 2007-2008*, The Worldwatch Institute, W.W. Norton & Company, 2007, p. 21

[16] From *An Experimental Analysis of Grid Sweep Searching*, by J. Wartes (Explorer Search and Rescue, Western Region, 1974).

[17] *The World Almanac and Book of Facts 2008*, (New York).

[18] Rosenzweig, M.L., *Species Diversity in Space and Time*, p. 292, (Cambridge: Cambridge University Press, 1995).

27. Table 1.6 gives the average weight, w, in pounds, of American men in their sixties for height, h, in inches.[19]

(a) How do you know that the data in this table could represent a linear function?

(b) Find weight, w, as a linear function of height, h. What is the slope of the line? What are the units for the slope?

(c) Find height, h, as a linear function of weight, w. What is the slope of the line? What are the units for the slope?

Table 1.6

h (inches)	68	69	70	71	72	73	74	75
w (pounds)	166	171	176	181	186	191	196	201

Problems 28–33 concern the maximum heart rate (MHR), which is the maximum number of times a person's heart can safely beat in one minute. If MHR is in beats per minute and a is age in years, the formulas used to estimate MHR, are

$$\text{For females: MHR} = 226 - a,$$

$$\text{For males: MHR} = 220 - a.$$

28. Which of the following is the correct statement?

(a) As you age, your maximum heart rate decreases by one beat per year.

(b) As you age, your maximum heart rate decreases by one beat per minute.

(c) As you age, your maximum heart rate decreases by one beat per minute per year.

29. Which of the following is the correct statement for a male and female of the same age?

(a) Their maximum heart rates are the same.

(b) The male's maximum heart rate exceeds the female's.

(c) The female's maximum heart rate exceeds the male's.

30. What can be said about the ages of a male and a female with the same maximum heart rate?

31. Recently[20] it has been suggested that a more accurate predictor of MHR for both males and females is given by

$$\text{MHR} = 208 - 0.7a.$$

(a) At what age do the old and new formulas give the same MHR for females? For males?

(b) Which of the following is true?

(i) The new formula predicts a higher MHR for young people and a lower MHR for older people than the old formula.

(ii) The new formula predicts a lower MHR for young people and a higher MHR for older people than the old formula.

(c) When testing for heart disease, doctors ask patients to walk on a treadmill while the speed and incline are gradually increased until their heart rates reach 85 percent of the MHR. For a 65-year-old male, what is the difference in beats per minute between the heart rate reached if the old formula is used and the heart rate reached if the new formula is used?

32. Experiments[21] suggest that the female MHR decreases by 12 beats per minute by age 21, and by 19 beats per minute by age 33. Is this consistent with MHR being approximately linear with age?

33. Experiments[22] suggest that the male MHR decreases by 9 beats per minute by age 21, and by 26 beats per minute by age 33. Is this consistent with MHR being approximately linear with age?

34. An Australian[23] study found that, if other factors are constant (education, experience, etc.), taller people receive higher wages for the same work. The study reported a "height premium" for men of 3% of the hourly wage for a 10 cm increase in height; for women the height premium reported was 2%. We assume that hourly wages are a linear function of height, with slope given by the height premium at the average hourly wage for that gender.

(a) The average hourly wage[24] for a 178 cm Australian man is AU\$29.40. Express the average hourly wage of an Australian man as a function of his height, x cm.

(b) The average hourly wage for a 164 cm Australian woman is AU\$24.78. Express the average hourly wage of an Australian woman as a function of her height, y cm.

(c) What is the difference in average hourly wages between men and women of height 178 cm?

(d) Is there a height for which men and women are predicted to have the same wage? If so, what is it?

[19] Adapted from "Average Weight of Americans by Height and Age," *The World Almanac* (New Jersey: Funk and Wagnalls, 1992), p. 956.
[20] www.physsportsmed.com/issues/2001/07_01/jul01news.htm, accessed January 4, 2005.
[21] www.css.edu/users/tboone2/asep/May2002JEPonline.html, accessed January 4, 2005.
[22] www.css.edu/users/tboone2/asep/May2002JEPonline.html, accessed January 4, 2005.
[23] "Study finds tall people at top of wages ladder", Yahoo News, May 17, 2009.
[24] Australian Fair Pay Commission, August 2007.

1.3 AVERAGE RATE OF CHANGE AND RELATIVE CHANGE

Average Rate of Change

In the previous section, we saw that the height of the winning Olympic pole vault increased at an approximately constant rate of 2 inches/year between 1900 and 1912. Similarly, the world record for the mile decreased at an approximately constant rate of 0.4 seconds/year. We now see how to calculate rates of change when they are not constant.

Example 1   Table 1.7 shows the height of the winning pole vault at the Olympics[25] during the 1960s and 1990s. Find the rate of change of the winning height between 1960 and 1968, and between 1992 and 2000. In which of these two periods did the height increase faster than during the period 1900–1912?

Table 1.7   *Winning height in men's Olympic pole vault (approximate)*

Year	1960	1964	1968	$\cdots$	1992	1996	2000
Height (inches)	185	201	213	$\cdots$	228	233	232

Solution   From 1900 to 1912, the height increased by 2 inches/year. To compare the 1960s and 1990s, we calculate

$$\begin{array}{c}\text{Average rate of change of height}\\ \text{1960 to 1968}\end{array} = \frac{\text{Change in height}}{\text{Change in time}} = \frac{213-185}{1968-1960} = 3.5 \text{ inches/year.}$$

$$\begin{array}{c}\text{Average rate of change of height}\\ \text{1992 to 2000}\end{array} = \frac{\text{Change in height}}{\text{Change in time}} = \frac{232-228}{2000-1992} = 0.5 \text{ inches/year.}$$

Thus, on average, the height was increasing more quickly during the 1960s than from 1900 to 1912. During the 1990s, the height was increasing more slowly than from 1900 to 1912.

In Example 1, the function does not have a constant rate of change (it is not linear). However, we can compute an *average rate of change* over any interval. The word average is used because the rate of change may vary within the interval. We have the following general formula.

If y is a function of t, so $y = f(t)$, then

$$\begin{array}{c}\textbf{Average rate of change} \text{ of } y\\ \text{between } t=a \text{ and } t=b\end{array} = \frac{\Delta y}{\Delta t} = \frac{f(b)-f(a)}{b-a}.$$

The units of average rate of change of a function are units of y per unit of t.

The average rate of change of a linear function is the slope, and a function is linear if the average rate of change is the same on all intervals.

---

[25] *The World Almanac and Book of Facts, 2005*, p. 866 (New York).

Example 2   Using Figure 1.25, estimate the average rate of change of the number of farms[26] in the US between 1950 and 1970.

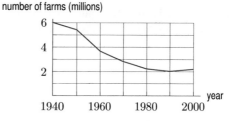

number of farms (millions)

Figure 1.25: Number of farms in the US (in millions)

Solution   Figure 1.25 shows that the number, N, of farms in the US was approximately 5.4 million in 1950 and approximately 2.8 million in 1970. If time, t, is in years, we have

$$\text{Average rate of change } = \frac{\Delta N}{\Delta t} = \frac{2.8 - 5.4}{1970 - 1950} = -0.13 \text{ million farms per year.}$$

The average rate of change is negative because the number of farms is decreasing. During this period, the number of farms decreased at an average rate of 0.13 million, or 130,000, per year.

We have looked at how an Olympic record and the number of farms change over time. In the next example, we look at average rate of change with respect to a quantity other than time.

Example 3   High levels of PCB (polychlorinated biphenyl, an industrial pollutant) in the environment affect pelicans' eggs. Table 1.8 shows that as the concentration of PCB in the eggshells increases, the thickness of the eggshell decreases, making the eggs more likely to break.[27]

Find the average rate of change in the thickness of the shell as the PCB concentration changes from 87 ppm to 452 ppm. Give units and explain why your answer is negative.

Table 1.8   *Thickness of pelican eggshells and PCB concentration in the eggshells*

Concentration, c, in parts per million (ppm)	87	147	204	289	356	452
Thickness, h, in millimeters (mm)	0.44	0.39	0.28	0.23	0.22	0.14

Solution   Since we are looking for the average rate of change of thickness with respect to change in PCB concentration, we have

$$\text{Average rate of change of thickness} = \frac{\text{Change in the thickness}}{\text{Change in the PCB level}} = \frac{\Delta h}{\Delta c} = \frac{0.14 - 0.44}{452 - 87}$$
$$= -0.00082 \frac{\text{mm}}{\text{ppm}}.$$

The units are thickness units (mm) over PCB concentration units (ppm), or millimeters over parts per million. The average rate of change is negative because the thickness of the eggshell decreases as the PCB concentration increases. The thickness of pelican eggs decreases by an average of 0.00082 mm for every additional part per million of PCB in the eggshell.

[26]*The World Almanac and Book of Facts, 2005*, p. 136 (New York).

[27]Risebrough, R. W., "Effects of environmental pollutants upon animals other than man." *Proceedings of the 6th Berkeley Symposium on Mathematics and Statistics, VI*, p. 443–463 (Berkeley: University of California Press, 1972).

Visualizing Rate of Change

For a function $y = f(x)$, the change in the value of the function between $x = a$ and $x = c$ is $\Delta y = f(c) - f(a)$. Since Δy is a difference of two y-values, it is represented by the vertical distance in Figure 1.26. The average rate of change of f between $x = a$ and $x = c$ is represented by the slope of the line joining the points A and C in Figure 1.27. This line is called the *secant line* between $x = a$ and $x = c$.

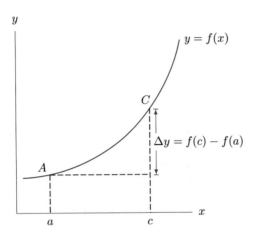

Figure 1.26: The change in a function is represented by a vertical distance

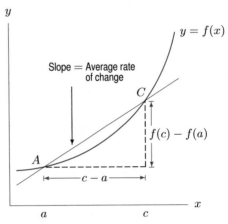

Figure 1.27: The average rate of change is represented by the slope of the line

Example 4 (a) Find the average rate of change of $y = f(x) = \sqrt{x}$ between $x = 1$ and $x = 4$.
(b) Graph $f(x)$ and represent this average rate of change as the slope of a line.
(c) Which is larger, the average rate of change of the function between $x = 1$ and $x = 4$ or the average rate of change between $x = 4$ and $x = 5$? What does this tell us about the graph of the function?

Solution (a) Since $f(1) = \sqrt{1} = 1$ and $f(4) = \sqrt{4} = 2$, between $x = 1$ and $x = 4$, we have

$$\text{Average rate of change} = \frac{\Delta y}{\Delta x} = \frac{f(4) - f(1)}{4 - 1} = \frac{2 - 1}{3} = \frac{1}{3}.$$

(b) A graph of $f(x) = \sqrt{x}$ is given in Figure 1.28. The average rate of change of f between 1 and 4 is the slope of the secant line between $x = 1$ and $x = 4$.
(c) Since the secant line between $x = 1$ and $x = 4$ is steeper than the secant line between $x = 4$ and $x = 5$, the average rate of change between $x = 1$ and $x = 4$ is larger than it is between $x = 4$ and $x = 5$. The rate of change is decreasing. This tells us that the graph of this function is bending downward.

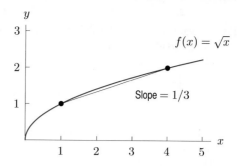

Figure 1.28: Average rate of change = Slope of secant line

Concavity

We now look at the graphs of functions whose rates of change are increasing throughout an interval or decreasing throughout an interval.

Figure 1.28 shows a graph that is bending downward because the rate of change is decreasing. The graph in Figure 1.26 bends upward because the rate of change of the function is increasing. We make the following definitions.

> The graph of a function is **concave up** if it bends upward as we move left to right; the graph is **concave down** if it bends downward. (See Figure 1.29.) A line is neither concave up nor concave down.

Figure 1.29: Concavity of a graph

Example 5　Using Figure 1.30, estimate the intervals over which:

(a) The function is increasing; decreasing.　　(b) The graph is concave up; concave down.

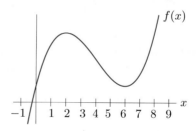

Figure 1.30

Solution　(a) The graph suggests that the function is increasing for $x < 2$ and for $x > 6$. It appears to be decreasing for $2 < x < 6$.

(b) The graph is concave down on the left and concave up on the right. It is difficult to tell exactly where the graph changes concavity, although it appears to be about $x = 4$. Approximately, the graph is concave down for $x < 4$ and concave up for $x > 4$.

Example 6   From the following values of $f(t)$, does f appear to be increasing or decreasing? Do you think its graph is concave up or concave down?

t	0	5	10	15	20	25	30
$f(t)$	12.6	13.1	14.1	16.2	20.0	29.6	42.7

Solution   Since the given values of $f(t)$ increase as t increases, f appears to be increasing. As we read from left to right, the change in $f(t)$ starts small and gets larger (for constant change in t), so the graph is climbing faster. Thus, the graph appears to be concave up. Alternatively, plot the points and notice that a curve through these points bends up.

Distance, Velocity, and Speed

A grapefruit is thrown up in the air. The height of the grapefruit above the ground first increases and then decreases. See Table 1.9.

Table 1.9   *Height, y, of the grapefruit above the ground t seconds after it is thrown*

t (sec)	0	1	2	3	4	5	6
y (feet)	6	90	142	162	150	106	30

Example 7   Find the change and average rate of change of the height of the grapefruit during the first 3 seconds. Give units and interpret your answers.

Solution   The change in height during the first 3 seconds is $\Delta y = 162 - 6 = 156$ ft. This means that the grapefruit goes up a total of 156 meters during the first 3 seconds. The average rate of change during this 3 second interval is $156/3 = 52$ ft/sec. During the first 3 seconds, the grapefruit is rising at an average rate of 52 ft/sec.

The average rate of change of height with respect to time is *velocity*. You may recognize the units (feet per second) as units of velocity.

$$\text{Average velocity} = \frac{\text{Change in distance}}{\text{Change in time}} = \frac{\text{Average rate of change of distance}}{\text{with respect to time}}$$

There is a distinction between *velocity* and *speed*. Suppose an object moves along a line. If we pick one direction to be positive, the velocity is positive if the object is moving in that direction and negative if it is moving in the opposite direction. For the grapefruit, upward is positive and downward is negative. Speed is the magnitude of velocity, so it is always positive or zero.

Example 8   Find the average velocity of the grapefruit over the interval $t = 4$ to $t = 6$. Explain the sign of your answer.

Solution   Since the height is $y = 150$ feet at $t = 4$ and $y = 30$ feet at $t = 6$, we have

$$\text{Average velocity} = \frac{\text{Change in distance}}{\text{Change in time}} = \frac{\Delta y}{\Delta t} = \frac{30 - 150}{6 - 4} = -60 \text{ ft/sec.}$$

The negative sign means the height is decreasing and the grapefruit is moving downward.

Example 9   A car travels away from home on a straight road. Its distance from home at time t is shown in Figure 1.31. Is the car's average velocity greater during the first hour or during the second hour?

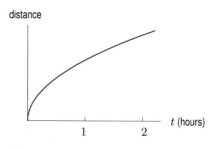

Figure 1.31: Distance of car from home   **Figure 1.32**: Average velocities of the car

Solution   Average velocity is represented by the slope of a secant line. Figure 1.32 shows that the secant line between $t = 0$ and $t = 1$ is steeper than the secant line between $t = 1$ and $t = 2$. Thus, the average velocity is greater during the first hour.

Relative Change

Is a population increase of 1000 a significant change? It depends on the original size of the community. If the town of Coyote, NM, population 1559, increases by 1000 people, the townspeople would definitely notice. On the other hand, if New York City, population 8.25 million, increases by 1000 people, almost no one will notice. To visualize the impact of the increase on the two different communities, we look at the change, 1000, as a fraction, or percentage, of the initial population. This percent change is called the *relative change*.

Example 10   If the population increases by 1000 people, find the relative change in the population for

(a) Coyote, NM (population 1559)
(b) New York City (population 8,250,000)

Solution   (a) The population increases by 1000 from 1559 so

$$\text{Relative change} = \frac{\text{Change in population}}{\text{Initial population}} = \frac{1000}{1559} = 0.641.$$

The population has increased by 64.1%, a significant increase.

(b) The population increases by 1000 from 8,250,000 so

$$\text{Relative change} = \frac{\text{Change in population}}{\text{Initial population}} = \frac{1000}{8,250,000} = 0.00012.$$

The population has increased by 0.012%, or less than one-tenth of one percent.

In general, when a quantity P changes from P_0 to P_1, we define

$$\text{Relative change in } P = \frac{\text{Change in } P}{P_0} = \frac{P_1 - P_0}{P_0}.$$

The relative change is a number, without units. It is often expressed as a percentage.

Example 11   A price increase can be significant or inconsequential depending on the item. In each of the following cases, find the relative change in price of a $2 price increase; give your answer as a percent.

(a)   A gallon of gas costing $2.25   (b)   A cell phone costing $180

Solution   (a) The change in the price is $2 so we have

$$\text{Relative change in price of gas} = \frac{\text{Change in price}}{\text{Initial price}} = \frac{2}{2.25} = 0.889.$$

The price of gas has gone up 88.9%.

(b) We have

$$\text{Relative change in price of cell phone} = \frac{\text{Change in price}}{\text{Initial price}} = \frac{2}{180} = 0.011.$$

The price of the cell phone has gone up only 1.1%.

Relative change can be positive or negative, as we see in the following example.

Example 12   Find the relative change in the price of a $75.99 pair of jeans if the sale price is $52.99.

Solution   The price has dropped from $75.99 to $52.99. We have

$$\text{Relative change} = \frac{52.99 - 75.99}{75.99} = \frac{-23}{75.99} = -0.303.$$

The price has been reduced by 30.3% for the sale.

Problems for Section 1.3

In Problems 1–4, decide whether the graph is concave up, concave down, or neither.

1.

2.

3.

4.

In Problems 5–8, find the relative, or percent, change.

5. S changes from 400 to 450

6. B changes from 12,000 to 15,000

7. R changes from 50 to 47

8. W changes from 0.3 to 0.05

9. Table 1.10 gives values of a function $w = f(t)$. Is this function increasing or decreasing? Is the graph of this function concave up or concave down?

Table 1.10

t	0	4	8	12	16	20	24
w	100	58	32	24	20	18	17

10. For which pairs of consecutive points in Figure 1.33 is the function graphed:

  (a) Increasing and concave up
  (b) Increasing and concave down
  (c) Decreasing and concave up
  (d) Decreasing and concave down

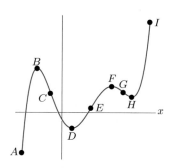

Figure 1.33

11. Graph a function $f(x)$ which is increasing everywhere and concave up for negative x and concave down for positive x.

12. Find the average rate of change of $f(x) = 2x^2$ between $x = 1$ and $x = 3$.

13. Find the average rate of change of $f(x) = 3x^2 + 4$ between $x = -2$ and $x = 1$. Illustrate your answer graphically.

14. When a deposit of $1000 is made into an account paying 8% interest, compounded annually, the balance, B, in the account after t years is given by $B = 1000(1.08)^t$. Find the average rate of change in the balance over the interval $t = 0$ to $t = 5$. Give units and interpret your answer in terms of the balance in the account.

15. Table 1.11 shows world bicycle production.[28]

  (a) Find the change in bicycle production between 1950 and 2000. Give units.
  (b) Find the average rate of change in bicycle production between 1950 and 2000. Give units and interpret your answer in terms of bicycle production.

Table 1.11   *World bicycle production, in millions*

Year	1950	1960	1970	1980	1990	2000
Bicycles	11	20	36	62	92	101

16. Table 1.12 gives the net sales of The Gap, Inc, which operates nearly 3000 clothing stores.[29]

  (a) Find the change in net sales between 2005 and 2008.
  (b) Find the average rate of change in net sales between 2005 and 2008. Give units and interpret your answer.
  (c) From 2003 to 2008, were there any one-year intervals during which the average rate of change was positive? If so, when?

Table 1.12   *Gap net sales, in millions of dollars*

Year	2003	2004	2005	2006	2007	2008
Sales	15,854	16,267	16,019	15,923	15,763	14,526

17. Table 1.13 shows attendance at NFL football games.[30]

  (a) Find the average rate of change in the attendance from 2003 to 2007. Give units.
  (b) Find the annual increase in the attendance for each year from 2003 to 2007. (Your answer should be four numbers.)
  (c) Show that the average rate of change found in part (a) is the average of the four yearly changes found in part (b).

Table 1.13   *Attendance at NFL football games, in millions of fans*

Year	2003	2004	2005	2006	2007
Attendance	21.64	21.71	21.79	22.20	22.26

18. Figure 1.34 shows the total value of US imports, in billions of dollars.[31]

  (a) Was the value of the imports higher in 1985 or in 2003? Approximately how much higher?
  (b) Estimate the average rate of change of US imports between 1985 and 2003. Give units and interpret your answer in terms of imports.

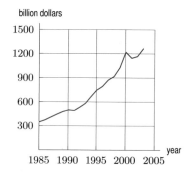

Figure 1.34

---

[28] www.earth-policy.org/Indicators/indicator11_data1.htm, accessed April 19, 2005.
[29] www.gapinc.com/public/investors/inv_financials.shtml/ accessed May 24, 2009.
[30] *Statistical Abstracts of the United States 2009*, Table 1204.
[31] www.ita.doc.gov/td/industry/otea/usfth/aggregate/H03t26.pdf, accessed April 19, 2005.

19. Table 1.14 gives sales of Pepsico, which operates two major businesses: beverages (including Pepsi) and snack foods.[32]

(a) Find the change in sales between 2003 and 2008.
(b) Find the average rate of change in sales between 2003 and 2008. Give units and interpret your answer.

Table 1.14   *Pepsico sales, in millions of dollars*

Year	2003	2004	2005	2006	2007	2008
Sales	26,971	29,261	32,562	35,137	39,474	45,251

20. Table 1.15 shows world population, P, in billions of people, world passenger automobile production, A, in millions of cars, and world cell phone subscribers, C, in millions of subscribers.[33]

(a) Find the average rate of change, with units, for each of P, A, and C between 1995 and 2005.
(b) Between 1995 and 2005, which increased faster:
   (i) Population or the number of automobiles?
   (ii) Population or the number of cell phone subscribers?

Table 1.15

Year	1995	2000	2005
P (billions)	5.68	6.07	6.45
A (millions)	36.1	41.3	45.9
C (millions)	91	740	2168

21. Figure 1.35 shows a particle's distance from a point. What is the particle's average velocity from $t = 0$ to $t = 3$?

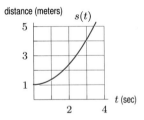

Figure 1.35

22. Figure 1.36 shows a particle's distance from a point. What is the particle's average velocity from $t = 1$ to $t = 3$?

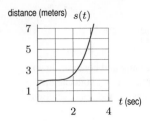

Figure 1.36

23. At time t in seconds, a particle's distance $s(t)$, in cm, from a point is given in the table. What is the average velocity of the particle from $t = 3$ to $t = 10$?

t	0	3	6	10	13
$s(t)$	0	72	92	144	180

24. Table 1.16 shows the production of tobacco in the US.[34]

(a) What is the average rate of change in tobacco production between 1996 and 2003? Give units and interpret your answer in terms of tobacco production.
(b) During this seven-year period, is there any interval during which the average rate of change was positive? If so, when?

Table 1.16   *Tobacco production, in millions of pounds*

Year	1996	1997	1998	1999	2000	2001	2002	2003
Production	1517	1787	1480	1293	1053	991	879	831

25. Do you expect the average rate of change (in units per year) of each of the following to be positive or negative? Explain your reasoning.

(a) Number of acres of rain forest in the world.
(b) Population of the world.
(c) Number of polio cases each year in the US, since 1950.
(d) Height of a sand dune that is being eroded.
(e) Cost of living in the US.

---

[32] www.pepsico.com, accessed May 23, 2009.
[33] *Vital Signs 2007-2008*, The Worldwatch Institute, W.W. Norton & Company, 2007, p. 51 and 67.
[34] *The World Almanac and Book of Facts 2005*, pp. 138–139 (New York).

26. Figure 1.37 shows the length, L, in cm, of a sturgeon (a type of fish) as a function of the time, t, in years.[35]

    (a) Is the function increasing or decreasing? Is the graph concave up or concave down?

    (b) Estimate the average rate of growth of the sturgeon between $t = 5$ and $t = 15$. Give units and interpret your answer in terms of the sturgeon.

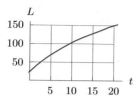

Figure 1.37

27. Table 1.17 shows the total US labor force, L. Find the average rate of change between 1940 and 2000; between 1940 and 1960; between 1980 and 2000. Give units and interpret your answers in terms of the labor force.[36]

Table 1.17 *US labor force, in thousands of workers*

Year	1940	1960	1980	2000
L	47,520	65,778	99,303	136,891

28. The total world marine catch[37] of fish, in metric tons, was 17 million in 1950 and 99 million in 2001. What was the average rate of change in the marine catch during this period? Give units and interpret your answer.

29. Table 1.18 gives the revenues, R, of General Motors, formerly the world's largest auto manufacturer.[38]

    (a) Find the change in revenues between 2003 and 2008.

    (b) Find the average rate of change in revenues between 2003 and 2008. Give units and interpret your answer.

    (c) From 2003 to 2008, were there any one-year intervals during which the average rate of change was negative? If so, which?

Table 1.18 *GM revenues, billions of dollars*

Year	2003	2004	2005	2006	2007	2008
R	184.0	192.9	193.1	205.6	181.1	149.0

30. The number of US households with cable television[39] was 12,168,450 in 1977 and 73,365,880 in 2003. Estimate the average rate of change in the number of US households with cable television during this 26-year period. Give units and interpret your answer.

31. Figure 1.7 in Problem 14 of Section 1.1 shows the amount of nicotine $N = f(t)$, in mg, in a person's bloodstream as a function of the time, t, in hours, since the last cigarette.

    (a) Is the average rate of change in nicotine level positive or negative? Explain.

    (b) Find the average rate of change in the nicotine level between $t = 0$ and $t = 3$. Give units and interpret your answer in terms of nicotine.

32. Table 1.19 shows the concentration, c, of creatinine in the bloodstream of a dog.[40]

    (a) Including units, find the average rate at which the concentration is changing between the

        (i) 6th and 8th minutes. (ii) 8th and 10th minutes.

    (b) Explain the sign and relative magnitudes of your results in terms of creatinine.

Table 1.19

t (minutes)	2	4	6	8	10
c (mg/ml)	0.439	0.383	0.336	0.298	0.266

33. The population of the world reached 1 billion in 1804, 2 billion in 1927, 3 billion in 1960, 4 billion in 1974, 5 billion in 1987 and 6 billion in 1999. Find the average rate of change of the population of the world, in people per minute, during each of these intervals (that is, from 1804 to 1927, 1927 to 1960, etc.).

Problems 34–35 refer to Figure 1.38 which shows the contraction velocity of a muscle as a function of the load it pulls against.

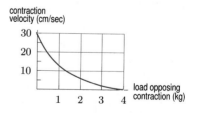

Figure 1.38

---

[35]Data from von Bertalanffy, L., *General System Theory*, p. 177 (New York: Braziller, 1968).

[36]*The World Almanac and Book of Facts 2005*, p. 144 (New York).

[37]*The World Almanac and Book of Facts 2005*, p. 143 (New York).

[38]www.gm.com/company/investor_information/earnings/hist_earnings/index.html, accessed May 23, 2009.

[39]*The World Almanac and Book of Facts 2005*, p. 310 (New York).

[40]From Cullen, M.R., *Linear Models in Biology* (Chichester: Ellis Horwood, 1985).

34. In terms of the muscle, interpret the

  (a) Vertical intercept   **(b)** Horizontal intercept

35. **(a)** Find the change in muscle contraction velocity when the load changes from 1 kg to 3 kg. Give units.
  (b) Find the average rate of change in the contraction velocity between 1 kg and 3 kg. Give units.

36. Table 1.20 gives the sales, S, of Intel Corporation, a leading manufacturer of integrated circuits.[41]

  (a) Find the change in sales between 2003 and 2008.
  (b) Find the average rate of change in sales between 2003 and 2008. Give units and interpret your answer.

Table 1.20   *Intel sales, in millions of dollars*

Year	2003	2004	2005	2006	2007	2008
S	30,100	34,200	38,800	35,400	38,300	37,600

37. In an experiment, a lizard is encouraged to run as fast as possible. Figure 1.39 shows the distance run in meters as a function of the time in seconds.[42]

  (a) If the lizard were running faster and faster, what would be the concavity of the graph? Does this match what you see?
  (b) Estimate the average velocity of the lizard during this 0.8 second experiment.

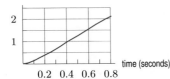

Figure 1.39

38. Values of $F(t)$, $G(t)$, and $H(t)$ are in Table 1.21. Which graph is concave up and which is concave down? Which function is linear?

Table 1.21

t	$F(t)$	$G(t)$	$H(t)$
10	15	15	15
20	22	18	17
30	28	21	20
40	33	24	24
50	37	27	29
60	40	30	35

39. Experiments suggest that the male maximum heart rate (the most times a male's heart can safely beat in a minute) decreases by 9 beats per minute during the first 21 years of his life, and by 26 beats per minute during the first 33 years.[43] If you model the maximum heart rate as a function of age, should you use a function that is increasing or decreasing, concave up or concave down?

40. A car starts slowly and then speeds up. Eventually the car slows down and stops. Graph the distance that the car has traveled against time.

41. Figure 1.40 shows the position of an object at time t.

  (a) Draw a line on the graph whose slope represents the average velocity between $t = 2$ and $t = 8$.
  (b) Is average velocity greater between $t = 0$ and $t = 3$ or between $t = 3$ and $t = 6$?
  (c) Is average velocity positive or negative between $t = 6$ and $t = 9$?

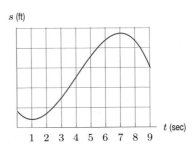

Figure 1.40

In Problems 42–45, which relative change is bigger in magnitude? Justify your answer.

42. The change in the Dow Jones average from 164.6 to 77.9 in 1931; the change in the Dow Jones average from 13261.8 to 8776.4 in 2008.

43. The change in the US population from 5.2 million to 7.2 million from 1800 to 1810; the change in the US population from 151.3 to 179.3 from 1950 to 1960.

44. An increase in class size from 5 to 10; an increase in class size from 30 to 50.

45. An increase in sales from \$100,000 to \$500,000; an increase in sales from \$20,000,000 to \$20,500,000.

46. Find the relative change of a population if it changes

  (a) From 1000 to 2000   **(b)** From 2000 to 1000
  (c) From 1,000,000 to 1,001,000

[41] Intel 2008 Annual Report, www.intel.com/intel/finance, accessed June 13, 2009.
[42] Data from Huey, R.B. and Hertz, P.E., "Effects of Body Size and Slope on the Acceleration of a Lizard," *J. Exp. Biol.*, Volume 110, 1984, p. 113-123.
[43] www.css.edu/users/tboone2/asep/May2002JEPonline.html, accessed January 4, 2005.

47. On Black Monday, October 28, 1929, the stock market on Wall Street crashed. The Dow Jones average dropped from 298.94 to 260.64 in one day. What was the relative change in the index?

48. On May 11, 2009, the cost to mail a letter in the US was raised from 42 cents to 44 cents. Find the relative change in the cost.

49. The US Consumer Price Index (CPI) is a measure of the cost of living. The inflation rate is the annual relative rate of change of the CPI. Use the January data in Table 1.22[44] to estimate the inflation rate for each of years 2005–2008.

50. During 2008 the US economy stopped growing and began to shrink. Table 1.23[45] gives quarterly data on the US Gross Domestic Product (GDP) which measures the size of the economy.

    (a) Estimate the relative growth rate (percent per year) at the first four times in the table.

    (b) Economists often say an economy is in recession if the GDP decreases for two quarters in a row. Was the US in recession in 2008?

Table 1.22

Year	2005	2006	2007	2008	2009
CPI	190.7	198.3	202.416	211.08	211.143

Table 1.23

t (years since 2008)	0	0.25	0.5	0.75	1.0
GDP (trillion dollars)	14.15	14.29	14.41	14.2	14.09

1.4 APPLICATIONS OF FUNCTIONS TO ECONOMICS

In this section, we look at some of the functions of interest to decision-makers in a firm or industry.

The Cost Function

> The **cost function**, $C(q)$, gives the total cost of producing a quantity q of some good.

What sort of function do you expect C to be? The more goods that are made, the higher the total cost, so C is an increasing function. Costs of production can be separated into two parts: the *fixed costs,* which are incurred even if nothing is produced, and the *variable costs,* which depend on how many units are produced.

An Example: Manufacturing Costs

Let's consider a company that makes radios. The factory and machinery needed to begin production are fixed costs, which are incurred even if no radios are made. The costs of labor and raw materials are variable costs since these quantities depend on how many radios are made. The fixed costs for this company are $24,000 and the variable costs are $7 per radio. Then,

$$\text{Total costs for the company} = \text{Fixed costs} + \text{Variable costs}$$
$$= 24{,}000 + 7 \cdot \text{Number of radios,}$$

so, if q is the number of radios produced,

$$C(q) = 24{,}000 + 7q.$$

This is the equation of a line with slope 7 and vertical intercept 24,000.

    The variable cost for one additional unit is called the *marginal cost.* For a linear cost function, the marginal cost is the rate of change, or slope, of the cost function.

---

[44]www.bls.gov/cpi, accessed June 7, 2009.
[45]www.bea.gov/national/nipaweb, Table 1.1.5.

Example 1   Graph the cost function $C(q) = 24{,}000 + 7q$. Label the fixed costs and marginal cost.

Solution   The graph of $C(q)$ is the line in Figure 1.41. The fixed costs are represented by the vertical intercept of 24,000. The marginal cost is represented by the slope of 7, which is the change in cost corresponding to a unit change in production.

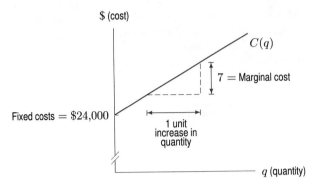

Figure 1.41: Cost function for the radio manufacturer

If $C(q)$ is a linear cost function,

- Fixed costs are represented by the vertical intercept.
- Marginal cost is represented by the slope.

Example 2   In each case, draw a graph of a linear cost function satisfying the given conditions:
(a) Fixed costs are large but marginal cost is small.
(b) There are no fixed costs but marginal cost is high.

Solution   (a) The graph is a line with a large vertical intercept and a small slope. See Figure 1.42.
(b) The graph is a line with a vertical intercept of zero (so the line goes through the origin) and a large positive slope. See Figure 1.43. Figures 1.42 and 1.43 have the same scales.

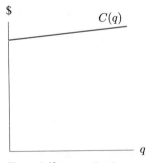

Figure 1.42: Large fixed costs, small marginal cost

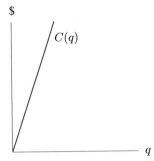

Figure 1.43: No fixed costs, high marginal cost

The Revenue Function

> The **revenue function**, $R(q)$, gives the total revenue received by a firm from selling a quantity, q, of some good.

If the good sells for a price of p per unit, and the quantity sold is q, then

$$\text{Revenue} = \text{Price} \cdot \text{Quantity}, \quad \text{so} \quad R = pq.$$

If the price does not depend on the quantity sold, so p is a constant, the graph of revenue as a function of q is a line through the origin, with slope equal to the price p.

Example 3   If radios sell for $15 each, sketch the manufacturer's revenue function. Show the price of a radio on the graph.

Solution   Since $R(q) = pq = 15q$, the revenue graph is a line through the origin with a slope of 15. See Figure 1.44. The price is the slope of the line.

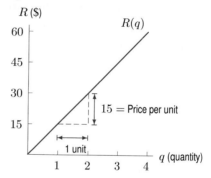

Figure 1.44: Revenue function for the radio manufacturer

Example 4   Graph the cost function $C(q) = 24{,}000 + 7q$ and the revenue function $R(q) = 15q$ on the same axes. For what values of q does the company make money?

Solution   The company makes money whenever revenues are greater than costs, so we find the values of q for which the graph of $R(q)$ lies above the graph of $C(q)$. See Figure 1.45.
We find the point at which the graphs of $R(q)$ and $C(q)$ cross:

$$\text{Revenue} = \text{Cost}$$
$$15q = 24{,}000 + 7q$$
$$8q = 24{,}000$$
$$q = 3000.$$

The company makes a profit if it produces and sells more than 3000 radios. The company loses money if it produces and sells fewer than 3000 radios.

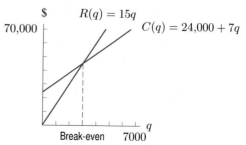

Figure 1.45: Cost and revenue functions for the radio manufacturer: What values of q generate a profit?

The Profit Function

Decisions are often made by considering the profit, usually written[46] as π to distinguish it from the price, p. We have

$$\boxed{\text{Profit} = \text{Revenue} - \text{Cost} \quad \text{so} \quad \pi = R - C.}$$

The *break-even point* for a company is the point where the profit is zero and revenue equals cost. See Figure 1.45.

Example 5   Find a formula for the profit function of the radio manufacturer. Graph it, marking the break-even point.

Solution   Since $R(q) = 15q$ and $C(q) = 24{,}000 + 7q$, we have

$$\pi(q) = R(q) - C(q) = 15q - (24{,}000 + 7q) = -24{,}000 + 8q.$$

Notice that the negative of the fixed costs is the vertical intercept and the break-even point is the horizontal intercept. See Figure 1.46.

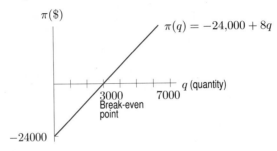

Figure 1.46: Profit for radio manufacturer

Example 6   (a) Using Table 1.24, estimate the break-even point for this company.
(b) Find the company's profit if 1000 units are produced.
(c) What price do you think the company is charging for its product?

Table 1.24   *Company's estimates of cost and revenue for a product*

q	500	600	700	800	900	1000	1100
$C(q)$, in $	5000	5500	6000	6500	7000	7500	8000
$R(q)$, in $	4000	4800	5600	6400	7200	8000	8800

Solution   (a) The break-even point is the value of q for which revenue equals cost. Since revenue is below cost at $q = 800$ and revenue is greater than cost at $q = 900$, the break-even point is between 800 and 900. The values in the table suggest that the break-even point is closer to 800, as the cost and revenue are closer there. A reasonable estimate for the break-even point is $q = 830$.
(b) If the company produces 1000 units, the cost is $7500 and the revenue is $8000, so the profit is $8000 - 7500 = 500$ dollars.
(c) From the table, it appears that $R(q) = 8q$. This indicates the company is selling the product for $8 each.

---

[46]This π has nothing to do with the area of a circle, and merely stands for the Greek equivalent of the letter "p."

The Marginal Cost, Marginal Revenue, and Marginal Profit

Just as we used the term marginal cost to mean the rate of change, or slope, of a linear cost function, we use the terms *marginal revenue* and *marginal profit* to mean the rate of change, or slope, of linear revenue and profit functions, respectively. The term *marginal* is used because we are looking at how the cost, revenue, or profit change "at the margin," that is, by the addition of one more unit. For example, for the radio manufacturer, the marginal cost is 7 dollars/item (the additional cost of producing one more item is $7), the marginal revenue is 15 dollars/item (the additional revenue from selling one more item is $15), and the marginal profit is 8 dollars/item (the additional profit from selling one more item is $8).

The Depreciation Function

Suppose that the radio manufacturer has a machine that costs $20,000 and is sold ten years later for $3000. We say the value of the machine *depreciates* from $20,000 today to a resale value of $3000 in ten years. The depreciation formula gives the value, $V(t)$, in dollars, of the machine as a function of the number of years, t, since the machine was purchased. We assume that the value of the machine depreciates linearly.

The value of the machine when it is new ($t = 0$) is $20,000, so $V(0) = 20,000$. The resale value at time $t = 10$ is $3000, so $V(10) = 3000$. We have

$$\text{Slope} = m = \frac{3000 - 20,000}{10 - 0} = \frac{-17,000}{10} = -1700 \text{ dollars per year.}$$

This slope tells us that the value of the machine is decreasing at a rate of $1700 per year. Since $V(0) = 20,000$, the vertical intercept is 20,000, so

$$V(t) = 20,000 - 1700t \text{ dollars.}$$

Supply and Demand Curves

The quantity, q, of an item that is manufactured and sold depends on its price, p. As the price increases, manufacturers are usually willing to supply more of the product, whereas the quantity demanded by consumers falls.

The **supply curve**, for a given item, relates the quantity, q, of the item that manufacturers are willing to make per unit time to the price, p, for which the item can be sold.
The **demand curve** relates the quantity, q, of an item demanded by consumers per unit time to the price, p, of the item.

Economists often think of the quantities supplied and demanded as functions of price. However, for historical reasons, the economists put price (the independent variable) on the vertical axis and quantity (the dependent variable) on the horizontal axis. (The reason for this state of affairs is that economists originally took price to be the dependent variable and put it on the vertical axis. Later, when the point of view changed, the axes did not.) Thus, typical supply and demand curves look like those shown in Figure 1.47.

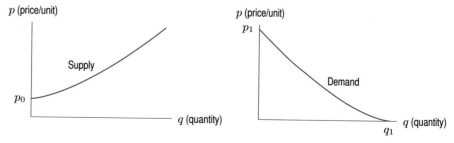

Figure 1.47: Supply and demand curves

Example 7   What is the economic meaning of the prices p_0 and p_1 and the quantity q_1 in Figure 1.47?

Solution   The vertical axis corresponds to a quantity of zero. Since the price p_0 is the vertical intercept on the supply curve, p_0 is the price at which the quantity supplied is zero. In other words, for prices below p_0, the suppliers will not produce anything. The price p_1 is the vertical intercept on the demand curve, so it corresponds to the price at which the quantity demanded is zero. In other words, for prices above p_1, consumers buy none of the product.

The horizontal axis corresponds to a price of zero, so the quantity q_1 on the demand curve is the quantity demanded if the price were zero—the quantity that could be given away free.

Equilibrium Price and Quantity

If we plot the supply and demand curves on the same axes, as in Figure 1.48, the graphs cross at the *equilibrium point*. The values p^* and q^* at this point are called the *equilibrium price* and *equilibrium quantity*, respectively. It is assumed that the market naturally settles to this equilibrium point. (See Problem 23.)

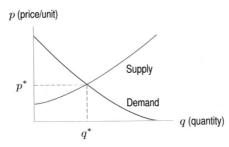

Figure 1.48: The equilibrium price and quantity

Example 8   Find the equilibrium price and quantity if

$$\text{Quantity supplied } = 3p - 50 \quad \text{and} \quad \text{Quantity demanded} = 100 - 2p.$$

Solution   To find the equilibrium price and quantity, we find the point at which

$$\text{Supply } = \text{Demand}$$
$$3p - 50 = 100 - 2p$$
$$5p = 150$$
$$p = 30.$$

The equilibrium price is $30. To find the equilibrium quantity, we use either the demand curve or the supply curve. At a price of $30, the quantity produced is $100 - 2 \cdot 30 = 40$ items. The equilibrium quantity is 40 items. In Figure 1.49, the demand and supply curves intersect at $p^* = 30$ and $q^* = 40$.

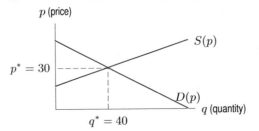

Figure 1.49: Equilibrium: $p^* = 30$, $q^* = 40$

The Effect of Taxes on Equilibrium

What effect do taxes have on the equilibrium price and quantity for a product? We distinguish between two types of taxes.[47] A *specific tax* is a fixed amount per unit of a product sold regardless of the selling price. This is the case with such items as gasoline, alcohol, and cigarettes. A specific tax is usually imposed on the producer. A *sales tax* is a fixed percentage of the selling price. Many cities and states collect sales tax on a wide variety of items. A sales tax is usually imposed on the consumer. We consider a specific tax now; a sales tax is considered in Problems 38 and 39.

Example 9   A specific tax of $5 per unit is now imposed upon suppliers in Example 8. What are the new equilibrium price and quantity?

Solution   The consumers pay p dollars per unit, but the suppliers receive only $p - 5$ dollars per unit because $5 goes to the government as taxes. Since

$$\text{Quantity supplied} = 3(\text{Amount per unit received by suppliers}) - 50,$$

the new supply equation is

$$\text{Quantity supplied} = 3(p - 5) - 50 = 3p - 65;$$

the demand equation is unchanged:

$$\text{Quantity demanded} = 100 - 2p.$$

At the equilibrium price, we have

$$\text{Demand} = \text{Supply}$$
$$100 - 2p = 3p - 65$$
$$165 = 5p$$
$$p = 33.$$

The equilibrium price is $33. The equilibrium quantity is 34 units, since the quantity demanded is $q = 100 - 2 \cdot 33 = 34$.

In Example 8, the equilibrium price was $30; with the imposition of a $5 tax in Example 9, the equilibrium price is $33. Thus the equilibrium price increases by $3 as a result of the tax. Notice that this is less than the amount of the tax. The consumer ends up paying $3 more than if the tax did not exist. However the government receives $5 per item. The producer pays the other $2 of the tax, retaining $28 of the price paid per item. Although the tax was imposed on the producer, some of the tax is passed on to the consumer in terms of higher prices. The tax has increased the price and reduced the number of items sold. See Figure 1.50. Notice that the taxes have the effect of moving the supply curve up by $5 because suppliers have to be paid $5 more to produce the same quantity.

---

[47]Adapted from Barry Bressler, *A Unified Approach to Mathematical Economics*, p. 81–88 (New York: Harper & Row, 1975).

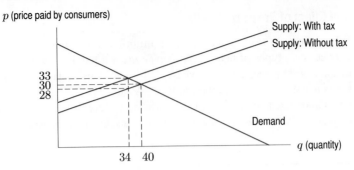

Figure 1.50: Specific tax shifts the supply curve, altering the equilibrium price and quantity

A Budget Constraint

An ongoing debate in the federal government concerns the allocation of money between defense and social programs. In general, the more that is spent on defense, the less that is available for social programs, and vice versa. Let's simplify the example to guns and butter. Assuming a constant budget, we show that the relationship between the number of guns and the quantity of butter is linear. Suppose that there is \$12,000 to be spent and that it is to be divided between guns, costing \$400 each, and butter, costing \$2000 a ton. Suppose the number of guns bought is g, and the number of tons of butter is b. Then the amount of money spent on guns is \$400g, and the amount spent on butter is \$2000b. Assuming all the money is spent,

$$\text{Amount spent on guns } + \text{ Amount spent on butter } = \$12,000$$

or

$$400g + 2000b = 12,000.$$

Thus, dividing both sides by 400,

$$g + 5b = 30.$$

This equation is the budget constraint. Since the budget constraint can be written as

$$g = 30 - 5b,$$

the graph of the budget constraint is a line. See Figure 1.51.

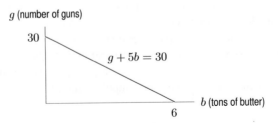

Figure 1.51: Budget constraint

Problems for Section 1.4

1. Figure 1.52 shows cost and revenue for a company.

   (a) Approximately what quantity does this company have to produce to make a profit?
   (b) Estimate the profit generated by 600 units.

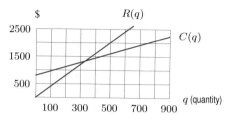

Figure 1.52

2. In Figure 1.53, which shows the cost and revenue functions for a product, label each of the following:

   (a) Fixed costs   (b) Break-even quantity

   (c) Quantities at which the company:
       (i) Makes a profit   (ii) Loses money

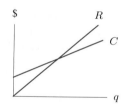

Figure 1.53

3. (a) Estimate the fixed costs and the marginal cost for the cost function in Figure 1.54.
   (b) Estimate $C(10)$ and interpret it in terms of cost.

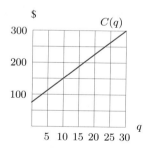

Figure 1.54

4. A company has cost and revenue functions, in dollars, given by $C(q) = 6000 + 10q$ and $R(q) = 12q$.

   (a) Find the cost and revenue if the company produces 500 units. Does the company make a profit? What about 5000 units?
   (b) Find the break-even point and illustrate it graphically.

5. Suppose that $q = f(p)$ is the demand curve for a product, where p is the selling price in dollars and q is the quantity sold at that price.

   (a) What does the statement $f(12) = 60$ tell you about demand for this product?
   (b) Do you expect this function to be increasing or decreasing? Why?

6. The demand curve for a quantity q of a product is $q = 5500 - 100p$ where p is price in dollars. Interpret the 5500 and the 100 in terms of demand. Give units.

7. A demand curve is given by $75p + 50q = 300$, where p is the price of the product, in dollars, and q is the quantity demanded at that price. Find p- and q-intercepts and interpret them in terms of consumer demand.

8. An amusement park charges an admission fee of $7 per person as well as an additional $1.50 for each ride.

   (a) For one visitor, find the park's total revenue $R(n)$ as a function of the number of rides, n, taken.
   (b) Find $R(2)$ and $R(8)$ and interpret your answers in terms of amusement park fees.

9. A company that makes Adirondack chairs has fixed costs of $5000 and variable costs of $30 per chair. The company sells the chairs for $50 each.

   (a) Find formulas for the cost and revenue functions.
   (b) Find the marginal cost and marginal revenue.
   (c) Graph the cost and the revenue functions on the same axes.
   (d) Find the break-even point.

10. A photocopying company has two different price lists. The first price list is $100 plus 3 cents per copy; the second price list is $200 plus 2 cents per copy.

    (a) For each price list, find the total cost as a function of the number of copies needed.
    (b) Determine which price list is cheaper for 5000 copies.
    (c) For what number of copies do both price lists charge the same amount?

11. A company has cost function $C(q) = 4000 + 2q$ dollars and revenue function $R(q) = 10q$ dollars.

    (a) What are the fixed costs for the company?
    (b) What is the marginal cost?
    (c) What price is the company charging for its product?
    (d) Graph $C(q)$ and $R(q)$ on the same axes and label the break-even point, q_0. Explain how you know the company makes a profit if the quantity produced is greater than q_0.
    (e) Find the break-even point q_0.

12. Values of a linear cost function are in Table 1.25. What are the fixed costs and the marginal cost? Find a formula for the cost function.

Table 1.25

q	0	5	10	15	20
$C(q)$	5000	5020	5040	5060	5080

13. A movie theater has fixed costs of $5000 per day and variable costs averaging $2 per customer. The theater charges $7 per ticket.

    (a) How many customers per day does the theater need in order to make a profit?
    (b) Find the cost and revenue functions and graph them on the same axes. Mark the break-even point.

14. A company producing jigsaw puzzles has fixed costs of $6000 and variable costs of $2 per puzzle. The company sells the puzzles for $5 each.

    (a) Find formulas for the cost function, the revenue function, and the profit function.
    (b) Sketch a graph of $R(q)$ and $C(q)$ on the same axes. What is the break-even point, q_0, for the company?

15. Production costs for manufacturing running shoes consist of a fixed overhead of $650,000 plus variable costs of $20 per pair of shoes. Each pair of shoes sells for $70.

    (a) Find the total cost, $C(q)$, the total revenue, $R(q)$, and the total profit, $\pi(q)$, as a function of the number of pairs of shoes produced, q.
    (b) Find the marginal cost, marginal revenue, and marginal profit.
    (c) How many pairs of shoes must be produced and sold for the company to make a profit?

16. The cost C, in millions of dollars, of producing q items is given by $C = 5.7 + 0.002q$. Interpret the 5.7 and the 0.002 in terms of production. Give units.

17. The table shows the cost of manufacturing various quantities of an item and the revenue obtained from their sale.

Quantity	0	10	20	30	40	50	60	70	80
Cost ($)	120	400	600	780	1000	1320	1800	2500	3400
Revenue ($)	0	300	600	900	1200	1500	1800	2100	2400

    (a) What range of production levels appears to be profitable?
    (b) Calculate the profit or loss for each of the quantities shown. Estimate the most profitable production level.

18. (a) Give an example of a possible company where the fixed costs are zero (or very small).
    (b) Give an example of a possible company where the marginal cost is zero (or very small).

19. A $15,000 robot depreciates linearly to zero in 10 years.

    (a) Find a formula for its value as a function of time.
    (b) How much is the robot worth three years after it is purchased?

20. A new bus worth $100,000 in 2010 depreciates linearly to $20,000 in 2030.

    (a) Find a formula for the value of the bus, V, as a function of time, t, in years since 2010.
    (b) What is the value of the bus in 2015?
    (c) Find and interpret the vertical and horizontal intercepts of the graph of the function.
    (d) What is the domain of the function?

21. A $50,000 tractor has a resale value of $10,000 twenty years after it was purchased. Assume that the value of the tractor depreciates linearly from the time of purchase.

    (a) Find a formula for the value of the tractor as a function of the time since it was purchased.
    (b) Graph the value of the tractor against time.
    (c) Find the horizontal and vertical intercepts, give units, and interpret them.

22. A corporate office provides the demand curve in Figure 1.55 to its ice cream shop franchises. At a price of $1.00 per scoop, 240 scoops per day can be sold.

    (a) Estimate how many scoops could be sold per day at a price of 50¢ per scoop. Explain.
    (b) Estimate how many scoops per day could be sold at a price of $1.50 per scoop. Explain.

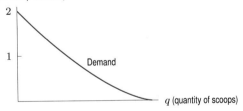

Figure 1.55

23. Figure 1.56 shows supply and demand for a product.

    (a) What is the equilibrium price for this product? At this price, what quantity is produced?
    (b) Choose a price above the equilibrium price—for example, $p = 12$. At this price, how many items are suppliers willing to produce? How many items do consumers want to buy? Use your answers to these questions to explain why, if prices are above the equilibrium price, the market tends to push prices lower (toward the equilibrium).

(c) Now choose a price below the equilibrium price—for example, $p = 8$. At this price, how many items are suppliers willing to produce? How many items do consumers want to buy? Use your answers to these questions to explain why, if prices are below the equilibrium price, the market tends to push prices higher (toward the equilibrium).

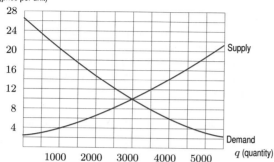

Figure 1.56

24. One of Tables 1.26 and 1.27 represents a supply curve; the other represents a demand curve.

    (a) Which table represents which curve? Why?

    (b) At a price of $155, approximately how many items would consumers purchase?

    (c) At a price of $155, approximately how many items would manufacturers supply?

    (d) Will the market push prices higher or lower than $155?

    (e) What would the price have to be if you wanted consumers to buy at least 20 items?

    (f) What would the price have to be if you wanted manufacturers to supply at least 20 items?

Table 1.26

p ($/unit)	182	167	153	143	133	125	118
q (quantity)	5	10	15	20	25	30	35

Table 1.27

p ($/unit)	6	35	66	110	166	235	316
q (quantity)	5	10	15	20	25	30	35

25. A company produces and sells shirts. The fixed costs are $7000 and the variable costs are $5 per shirt.

    (a) Shirts are sold for $12 each. Find cost and revenue as functions of the quantity of shirts, q.

    (b) The company is considering changing the selling price of the shirts. Demand is $q = 2000 - 40p$, where p is price in dollars and q is the number of shirts. What quantity is sold at the current price of $12? What profit is realized at this price?

    (c) Use the demand equation to write cost and revenue as functions of the price, p. Then write profit as a function of price.

    (d) Graph profit against price. Find the price that maximizes profits. What is this profit?

26. When the price, p, charged for a boat tour was $25, the average number of passengers per week, N, was 500. When the price was reduced to $20, the average number of passengers per week increased to 650. Find a formula for the demand curve, assuming that it is linear.

27. Table 1.28 gives data for the linear demand curve for a product, where p is the price of the product and q is the quantity sold every month at that price. Find formulas for the following functions. Interpret their slopes in terms of demand.

    (a) q as a function of p.   **(b)** p as a function of q.

Table 1.28

p (dollars)	16	18	20	22	24
q (tons)	500	460	420	380	340

28. The demand curve for a product is given by $q = 120,000 - 500p$ and the supply curve is given by $q = 1000p$ for $0 \leq q \leq 120,000$, where price is in dollars.

    (a) At a price of $100, what quantity are consumers willing to buy and what quantity are producers willing to supply? Will the market push prices up or down?

    (b) Find the equilibrium price and quantity. Does your answer to part (a) support the observation that market forces tend to push prices closer to the equilibrium price?

29. World production, Q, of zinc in thousands of metric tons and the value, P, in dollars per metric ton are given[48] in Table 1.29. Plot the value as a function of production. Sketch a possible supply curve.

Table 1.29 *World zinc production*

Year	2003	2004	2005	2006	2007
Q	9520	9590	9930	10,000	10,900
P	896	1160	1480	3500	3400

[48]http://minerals.usgs.gov/ds/2005/140/, accessed May 24, 2009.

30. A taxi company has an annual budget of $720,000 to spend on drivers and car replacement. Drivers cost the company $30,000 each and car replacements cost $20,000 each.

   (a) What is the company's budget constraint equation? Let d be the number of drivers paid and c be the number of cars replaced.
   (b) Find and interpret both intercepts of the graph of the equation.

31. You have a budget of $1000 for the year to cover your books and social outings. Books cost (on average) $40 each and social outings cost (on average) $10 each. Let b denote the number of books purchased per year and s denote the number of social outings in a year.

   (a) What is the equation of your budget constraint?
   (b) Graph the budget constraint. (It does not matter which variable you put on which axis.)
   (c) Find the vertical and horizontal intercepts, and give a financial interpretation for each.

32. A company has a total budget of $500,000 and spends this budget on raw materials and personnel. The company uses m units of raw materials, at a cost of $100 per unit, and hires r employees, at a cost of $25,000 each.

   (a) What is the equation of the company's budget constraint?
   (b) Solve for m as a function of r.
   (c) Solve for r as a function of m.

33. Linear supply and demand curves are shown in Figure 1.57, with price on the vertical axis.

   (a) Label the equilibrium price p_0 and the equilibrium quantity q_0 on the axes.
   (b) Explain the effect on equilibrium price and quantity if the slope, $\Delta p/\Delta q$, of the supply curve increases. Illustrate your answer graphically.
   (c) Explain the effect on equilibrium price and quantity if the slope, $\Delta p/\Delta q$, of the demand curve becomes more negative. Illustrate your answer graphically.

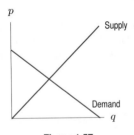

Figure 1.57

34. A demand curve has equation $q = 100 - 5p$, where p is price in dollars. A $2 tax is imposed on consumers. Find the equation of the new demand curve. Sketch both curves.

35. A supply curve has equation $q = 4p - 20$, where p is price in dollars. A $2 tax is imposed on suppliers. Find the equation of the new supply curve. Sketch both curves.

36. A tax of $8 per unit is imposed on the supplier of an item. The original supply curve is $q = 0.5p - 25$ and the demand curve is $q = 165 - 0.5p$, where p is price in dollars. Find the equilibrium price and quantity before and after the tax is imposed.

37. The demand and supply curves for a product are given in terms of price, p, by

$$q = 2500 - 20p \quad \text{and} \quad q = 10p - 500.$$

   (a) Find the equilibrium price and quantity. Represent your answers on a graph.
   (b) A specific tax of $6 per unit is imposed on suppliers. Find the new equilibrium price and quantity. Represent your answers on the graph.
   (c) How much of the $6 tax is paid by consumers and how much by producers?
   (d) What is the total tax revenue received by the government?

38. In Example 8, the demand and supply curves are given by $q = 100 - 2p$ and $q = 3p - 50$, respectively; the equilibrium price is $30 and the equilibrium quantity is 40 units. A sales tax of 5% is imposed on the consumer.

   (a) Find the equation of the new demand and supply curves.
   (b) Find the new equilibrium price and quantity.
   (c) How much is paid in taxes on each unit? How much of this is paid by the consumer and how much by the producer?
   (d) How much tax does the government collect?

39. Answer the questions in Problem 38, assuming that the 5% sales tax is imposed on the supplier instead of the consumer.

1.5 EXPONENTIAL FUNCTIONS

The function $f(x) = 2^x$, where the power is variable, is an *exponential function*. The number 2 is called the base. Exponential functions of the form $f(x) = k \cdot a^x$, where a is a positive constant, are used to represent many phenomena in the natural and social sciences.

Population Growth

The population of Nevada[49] from 2000 to 2006 is given in Table 1.30. To see how the population is growing, we look at the increase in population in the third column of Table 1.30. If the population had been growing linearly, all the numbers in the third column would be the same. But populations usually grow much faster as they get bigger, so it is not surprising that the numbers in the third column increase.

Table 1.30 *Population of Nevada (estimated), 2000–2006*

Year	Population (millions)	Change in population (millions)
2000	2.020	
		0.073
2001	2.093	
		0.075
2002	2.168	
		0.078
2003	2.246	
		0.081
2004	2.327	
		0.084
2005	2.411	
		0.087
2006	2.498	

Suppose we divide each year's population by the previous year's population. We get, approximately,

$$\frac{\text{Population in 2001}}{\text{Population in 2000}} = \frac{2.093 \text{ million}}{2.020 \text{ million}} = 1.036$$

$$\frac{\text{Population in 2002}}{\text{Population in 2001}} = \frac{2.168 \text{ million}}{2.093 \text{ million}} = 1.036.$$

$$\frac{\text{Population in 2003}}{\text{Population in 2002}} = \frac{2.246 \text{ million}}{2.168 \text{ million}} = 1.036.$$

The fact that all calculations are near 1.036 shows the population grew by about 3.6% between 2000 and 2001, between 2001 and 2002, and between 2002 and 2003. Whenever we have a constant percent increase (here 3.6%), we have *exponential growth*. If t is the number of years since 2000 and population is in millions,

When $t = 0$, population $= 2.020 = 2.020(1.036)^0$.

When $t = 1$, population $= 2.093 = 2.020(1.036)^1$.

When $t = 2$, population $= 2.168 = 2.093(1.036) = 2.020(1.036)^2$.

When $t = 3$, population $= 2.246 = 2.168(1.036) = 2.020(1.036)^3$.

So P, the population in millions t years after 2000, is given by

$$P = 2.020(1.036)^t \text{ million.}$$

Since the variable t is in the exponent, this is an exponential function. The base, 1.036, represents the factor by which the population grows each year and is called the *growth factor*. Assuming that the formula holds for 50 years, the population graph has the shape in Figure 1.58. The population is growing, so the function is increasing. Since the population grows faster as time passes, the graph is concave up. This behavior is typical of an exponential function. Even exponential functions that climb slowly at first, such as this one, eventually climb extremely quickly.

---

[49]www.census.gov, accessed May 14, 2007.

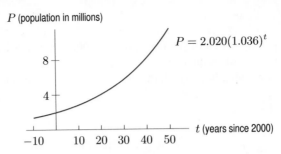

Figure 1.58: Population of Nevada (estimated): Exponential growth

Elimination of a Drug from the Body

Now we look at a quantity that is decreasing instead of increasing. When a patient is given medication, the drug enters the bloodstream. The rate at which the drug is metabolized and eliminated depends on the particular drug. For the antibiotic ampicillin, approximately 40% of the drug is eliminated every hour. A typical dose of ampicillin is 250 mg. Suppose $Q = f(t)$, where Q is the quantity of ampicillin, in mg, in the bloodstream at time t hours since the drug was given. At $t = 0$, we have $Q = 250$. Since the quantity remaining at the end of each hour is 60% of the quantity remaining the hour before, we have

$$f(0) = 250$$
$$f(1) = 250(0.6)$$
$$f(2) = 250(0.6)(0.6) = 250(0.6)^2$$
$$f(3) = 250(0.6)^2(0.6) = 250(0.6)^3.$$

So, after t hours,

$$Q = f(t) = 250(0.6)^t.$$

This function is called an *exponential decay* function. As t increases, the function values get arbitrarily close to zero. The t-axis is a *horizontal asymptote* for this function.

Notice the way the values in Table 1.31 are decreasing. Each additional hour a smaller quantity of drug is removed than the previous hour (100 mg the first hour, 60 mg the second, and so on). This is because as time passes, there is less of the drug in the body to be removed. Thus, the graph in Figure 1.59 bends upward. Compare this to the exponential growth in Figure 1.58, where each step upward is larger than the previous one. Notice that both graphs are concave up.

Table 1.31 *Value of decay function*

t (hours)	Q (mg)
0	250
1	150
2	90
3	54
4	32.4
5	19.4

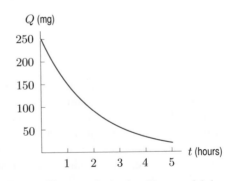

Figure 1.59: Drug elimination: Exponential decay

The General Exponential Function

Exponential growth is often described in terms of percent growth rates. The population of Nevada is growing at 3.6% per year, so it increases by a factor of $a = 1 + 0.036 = 1.036$ every year. Similarly, 40% of the ampicillin is removed every hour, so the quantity remaining decays by a factor of $a = 1 - 0.40 = 0.6$ each hour. We have the following general formulas.

We say that P is an **exponential function** of t with base a if

$$P = P_0 a^t,$$

where P_0 is the initial quantity (when $t = 0$) and a is the factor by which P changes when t increases by 1. If $a > 1$, we have **exponential growth**; if $0 < a < 1$, we have **exponential decay**. The factor a is given by

$$a = 1 + r$$

where r is the decimal representation of the percent rate of change; r may be positive (for growth) or negative (for decay).

The largest possible domain for the exponential function is all real numbers,[50] provided $a > 0$.

Comparison Between Linear and Exponential Functions

Every exponential function changes at a constant percent, or *relative*, rate. For example, the population of Nevada increased approximately 3.6% per year. Every linear function changes at a constant absolute rate. For example, the Olympic pole vault record increased by 2 inches per year.

A **linear** function has a constant rate of change.
An **exponential** function has a constant percent, or relative, rate of change.

Example 1 The amount of adrenaline in the body can change rapidly. Suppose the initial amount is 15 mg. Find a formula for A, the amount in mg, at a time t minutes later if A is:

(a) Increasing by 0.4 mg per minute. (b) Decreasing by 0.4 mg per minute.
(c) Increasing by 3% per minute. (d) Decreasing by 3% per minute.

Solution (a) This is a linear function with initial quantity 15 and slope 0.4, so

$$A = 15 + 0.4t.$$

(b) This is a linear function with initial quantity 15 and slope -0.4, so

$$A = 15 - 0.4t.$$

(c) This is an exponential function with initial quantity 15 and base $1 + 0.03 = 1.03$, so

$$A = 15(1.03)^t.$$

(d) This is an exponential function with initial quantity 15 and base $1 - 0.03 = 0.97$, so

$$A = 15(0.97)^t.$$

---

[50]The reason we do not want $a \leq 0$ is that, for example, we cannot define $a^{1/2}$ if $a < 0$. Also, we do not usually have $a = 1$, since $P = P_0 a^t = P_0 1^t = P_0$ is then a constant function.

Example 2

Sales[51] at Borders Books and Music stores increased from $2503 million in 1997 to $3699 million in 2003. Assuming that sales have been increasing exponentially, find an equation of the form $P = P_0 a^t$, where P is Borders sales in millions of dollars and t is the number of years since 1997. What is the percent growth rate?

Solution

We know that $P = 2503$ when $t = 0$, so $P_0 = 2503$. To find a, we use the fact that $P = 3699$ when $t = 6$. Substituting gives

$$P = P_0 a^t$$
$$3699 = 2503a^6.$$

Dividing both sides by 2503, we get

$$\frac{3699}{2503} = a^6$$
$$1.478 = a^6.$$

Taking the sixth root of both sides gives

$$a = (1.478)^{1/6} = 1.07.$$

Since $a = 1.07$, the equation for Borders sales as a function of the number of years since 1997 is

$$P = 2503(1.07)^t.$$

During this period, sales increased by 7% per year.

> **Recognizing Data from an Exponential Function**: Values of t and P in a table could come from an exponential function $P = P_0 a^t$ if ratios of P values are constant for equally spaced t values.

Example 3

Which of the following tables of values could correspond to an exponential function, a linear function, or neither? For those which could correspond to an exponential or linear function, find a formula for the function.

(a)

x	$f(x)$
0	16
1	24
2	36
3	54
4	81

(b)

x	$g(x)$
0	14
1	20
2	24
3	29
4	35

(c)

x	$h(x)$
0	5.3
1	6.5
2	7.7
3	8.9
4	10.1

Solution

(a) We see that f cannot be a linear function, since $f(x)$ increases by different amounts ($24 - 16 = 8$ and $36 - 24 = 12$) as x increases by one. Could f be an exponential function? We look at the ratios of successive $f(x)$ values:

$$\frac{24}{16} = 1.5 \qquad \frac{36}{24} = 1.5 \qquad \frac{54}{36} = 1.5 \qquad \frac{81}{54} = 1.5.$$

Since the ratios are all equal to 1.5, this table of values could correspond to an exponential function with a base of 1.5. Since $f(0) = 16$, a formula for $f(x)$ is

$$f(x) = 16(1.5)^x.$$

Check by substituting $x = 0, 1, 2, 3, 4$ into this formula; you get the values given for $f(x)$.

(b) As x increases by one, $g(x)$ increases by 6 (from 14 to 20), then 4 (from 20 to 24), so g is not linear. We check to see if g could be exponential:

---

[51]http://phx.corporate-ir.net/phoenix.zhtml?c=65380&p=irol-annualreports, accessed April 14, 2005.

$$\frac{20}{14} = 1.43 \quad \text{and} \quad \frac{24}{20} = 1.2.$$

Since these ratios (1.43 and 1.2) are different, g is not exponential.

(c) For h, notice that as x increases by one, the value of $h(x)$ increases by 1.2 each time. So h could be a linear function with a slope of 1.2. Since $h(0) = 5.3$, a formula for $h(x)$ is

$$h(x) = 5.3 + 1.2x.$$

The Family of Exponential Functions and the Number e

The formula $P = P_0 a^t$ gives a family of exponential functions with parameters P_0 (the initial quantity) and a (the base). The base tells us whether the function is increasing ($a > 1$) or decreasing ($0 < a < 1$). Since a is the factor by which P changes when t is increased by 1, large values of a mean fast growth; values of a near 0 mean fast decay. (See Figures 1.60 and 1.61.) All members of the family $P = P_0 a^t$ are concave up if $P_0 > 0$.

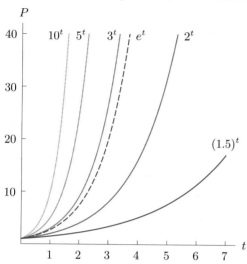

Figure 1.60: Exponential growth: $P = a^t$, for $a > 1$ **Figure 1.61**: Exponential decay: $P = a^t$, for $0 < a < 1$

In practice the most commonly used base is the number $e = 2.71828\ldots$. The fact that most calculators have an e^x button is an indication of how important e is. Since e is between 2 and 3, the graph of $y = e^t$ in Figure 1.60 is between the graphs of $y = 2^t$ and $y = 3^t$.

The base e is used so often that it is called the natural base. At first glance, this is somewhat mysterious: What could be natural about using 2.71828... as a base? The full answer to this question must wait until Chapter 3, where you will see that many calculus formulas come out more neatly when e is used as the base. (See Appendix B for the relation to compound interest.)

Problems for Section 1.5

1. The following functions give the populations of four towns with time t in years.

(i) $P = 600(1.12)^t$ (ii) $P = 1,000(1.03)^t$
(iii) $P = 200(1.08)^t$ (iv) $P = 900(0.90)^t$

(a) Which town has the largest percent growth rate? What is the percent growth rate?
(b) Which town has the largest initial population? What is that initial population?
(c) Are any of the towns decreasing in size? If so, which one(s)?

2. Each of the following functions gives the amount of a substance present at time t. In each case, give the amount present initially (at $t = 0$), state whether the function represents exponential growth or decay, and give the percent growth or decay rate.

(a) $A = 100(1.07)^t$ **(b)** $A = 5.3(1.054)^t$
(c) $A = 3500(0.93)^t$ **(d)** $A = 12(0.88)^t$

3. Figure 1.62 shows graphs of several cities' populations against time. Match each of the following descriptions to a graph and write a description to match each of the remaining graphs.

    (a) The population increased at 5% per year.
    (b) The population increased at 8% per year.
    (c) The population increased by 5000 people per year.
    (d) The population was stable.

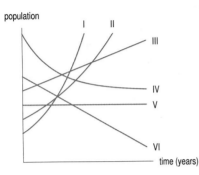

Figure 1.62

4. A town has a population of 1000 people at time $t = 0$. In each of the following cases, write a formula for the population, P, of the town as a function of year t.

    (a) The population increases by 50 people a year.
    (b) The population increases by 5% a year.

5. The gross domestic product, G, of Switzerland was 310 billion dollars in 2007. Give a formula for G (in billions of dollars) t years after 2007 if G increases by
    (a)   3% per year   **(b)**   8 billion dollars per year

6. A product costs $80 today. How much will the product cost in t days if the price is reduced by

    (a) $4 a day   **(b)**   5% a day

7. An air-freshener starts with 30 grams and evaporates. In each of the following cases, write a formula for the quantity, Q grams, of air-freshener remaining t days after the start and sketch a graph of the function. The decrease is:

    (a)   2 grams a day   **(b)**   12% a day

8. World population is approximately $P = 6.4(1.0126)^t$, with P in billions and t in years since 2004.

    (a) What is the yearly percent rate of growth of the world population?
    (b) What was the world population in 2004? What does this model predict for the world population in 2010?
    (c) Use part (b) to find the average rate of change of the world population between 2004 and 2010.

9. A 50 mg dose of quinine is given to a patient to prevent malaria. Quinine leaves the body at a rate of 6% per hour.

    (a) Find a formula for the amount, A (in mg), of quinine in the body t hours after the dose is given.
    (b) How much quinine is in the body after 24 hours?
    (c) Graph A as a function of t.
    (d) Use the graph to estimate when 5 mg of quinine remains.

10. The Hershey Company is the largest US producer of chocolate. In 2008, annual net sales were 5.1 billion dollars and were increasing at a continuous rate of 4.3% per year.[52]

    (a) Write a formula for annual net sales, S, as a function of time, t, in years since 2008.
    (b) Estimate annual net sales in 2015.
    (c) Use a graph or trial and error to estimate the year in which annual net sales are expected to pass 8 billion dollars.

11. The consumer price index (CPI) for a given year is the amount of money in that year that has the same purchasing power as $100 in 1983. At the start of 2009, the CPI was 211. Write a formula for the CPI as a function of t, years after 2009, assuming that the CPI increases by 2.8% every year.

12. During the 1980s, Costa Rica had the highest deforestation rate in the world, at 2.9% per year. (This is the rate at which land covered by forests is shrinking.) Assuming the rate continues, what percent of the land in Costa Rica covered by forests in 1980 will be forested in 2015?

13. **(a)** Make a table of values for $y = e^x$ using $x = 0, 1, 2, 3$.
    (b) Plot the points found in part (a). Does the graph look like an exponential growth or decay function?
    (c) Make a table of values for $y = e^{-x}$ using $x = 0, 1, 2, 3$.
    (d) Plot the points found in part (c). Does the graph look like an exponential growth or decay function?

14. Graph $y = 100e^{-0.4x}$. Describe what you see.

For Problems 15–16, find a possible formula for the function represented by the data.

15.

x	0	1	2	3
$f(x)$	4.30	6.02	8.43	11.80

16.

t	0	1	2	3
$g(t)$	5.50	4.40	3.52	2.82

[52]2008 Annual Report to Stockholders, accessed at www.thehersheycompany.com.

Give a possible formula for the functions in Problems 17–18.

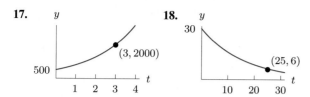

17.

18.

x	$f(x)$	$g(x)$	$h(x)$
-2	12	16	37
-1	17	24	34
0	20	36	31
1	21	54	28
2	18	81	25

19. If the world's population increased exponentially from 4.453 billion in 1980 to 5.937 billion in 1998 and continued to increase at the same percentage rate between 1998 and 2008, calculate what the world's population would have been in 2008. How does this compare to the actual population of 6.771 billion?

20. The number of passengers using a railway fell from 190,205 to 174,989 during a 5-year period. Find the annual percentage decrease over this period.

21. The company that produces Cliffs Notes (abridged versions of classic literature) was started in 1958 with $4000 and sold in 1998 for $14,000,000. Find the annual percent increase in the value of this company over the 40 years.

22. Find a formula for the number of zebra mussels in a bay as a function of the number of years since 2003, given that there were 2700 at the start of 2003 and 3186 at the start of 2004.

    (a) Assume that the number of zebra mussels is growing linearly. Give units for the slope of the line and interpret it in terms of zebra mussels.

    (b) Assume that the number of zebra mussels is growing exponentially. What is the percent rate of growth of the zebra mussel population?

23. Worldwide, wind energy[53] generating capacity, W, was 40,300 megawatts in 2003 and 121,188 megawatts in 2008.

    (a) Use the values given to write W, in megawatts, as a linear function of t, the number of years since 2003.

    (b) Use the values given to write W as an exponential function of t.

    (c) Graph the functions found in parts (a) and (b) on the same axes. Label the given values.

24. **(a)** Which (if any) of the functions in the following table could be linear? Find formulas for those functions.

    (b) Which (if any) of these functions could be exponential? Find formulas for those functions.

25. Determine whether each of the following tables of values could correspond to a linear function, an exponential function, or neither. For each table of values that could correspond to a linear or an exponential function, find a formula for the function.

(a)

x	$f(x)$
0	10.5
1	12.7
2	18.9
3	36.7

(b)

t	$s(t)$
-1	50.2
0	30.12
1	18.072
2	10.8432

(c)

u	$g(u)$
0	27
2	24
4	21
6	18

26. **(a)** Could the data on annual world soybean production[54] in Table 1.32 correspond to a linear function or an exponential function? If so, which?

    (b) Find a formula for P, world soybean production in millions of tons, as a function of time, t, in years since 2000.

    (c) What is the annual percent increase in soybean production?

Table 1.32 *Soybean production, in millions of tons*

Year	2000	2001	2002	2003	2004	2005
Production	161.0	170.3	180.2	190.7	201.8	213.5

27. The 2004 US presidential debates questioned whether the minimum wage has kept pace with inflation. Decide the question using the following information:[55] In 1938, the minimum wage was 25¢; in 2004, it was $5.15. During the same period, inflation averaged 4.3%.

28. **(a)** Niki invested $10,000 in the stock market. The investment was a loser, declining in value 10% per year each year for 10 years. How much was the investment worth after 10 years?

    (b) After 10 years, the stock began to gain value at 10% per year. After how long will the investment regain its initial value ($10,000)?

---

[53]World Wind Energy Report 2008, WWEA.
[54]*Vital Signs 2007-2008*, The Worldwatch Institute, W.W. Norton & Company, 2007, p. 23.
[55]http://www.dol.gov/esa/minwage/chart.htm#5.

29. A photocopy machine can reduce copies to 80% of their original size. By copying an already reduced copy, further reductions can be made.

  (a) If a page is reduced to 80%, what percent enlargement is needed to return it to its original size?

  (b) Estimate the number of times in succession that a page must be copied to make the final copy less than 15% of the size of the original.

30. Whooping cough was thought to have been almost wiped out by vaccinations. It is now known that the vaccination wears off, leading to an increase in the number of cases, w, from 1248 in 1981 to 18,957 in 2004.

  (a) With t in years since 1980, find an exponential function that fits this data.

  (b) What does your answer to part (a) give as the average annual percent growth rate of the number of cases?

  (c) On May 4, 2005, the *Arizona Daily Star* reported (correctly) that the number of cases had more than doubled between 2000 and 2004. Does your model confirm this report? Explain.

31. Aircraft require longer takeoff distances, called takeoff rolls, at high altitude airports because of diminished air density. The table shows how the takeoff roll for a certain light airplane depends on the airport elevation. (Takeoff rolls are also strongly influenced by air temperature; the data shown assume a temperature of $0°$ C.) Determine a formula for this particular aircraft that gives the takeoff roll as an exponential function of airport elevation.

Elevation (ft)	Sea level	1000	2000	3000	4000
Takeoff roll (ft)	670	734	805	882	967

1.6   THE NATURAL LOGARITHM

In Section 1.5, we projected the population of Nevada (in millions) by the function

$$P = f(t) = 2.020(1.036)^t,$$

where t is the number of years since 2000. Now suppose that instead of calculating the population at time t, we ask when the population will reach 4 million. We want to find the value of t for which

$$4 = f(t) = 2.020(1.036)^t.$$

We use logarithms to solve for a variable in an exponent.

Definition and Properties of the Natural Logarithm

We define the natural logarithm of x, written $\ln x$, as follows:

> The **natural logarithm** of x, written $\ln x$, is the power of e needed to get x. In other words,
>
> $$\ln x = c \quad \text{means} \quad e^c = x.$$
>
> The natural logarithm is sometimes written $\log_e x$.

For example, $\ln e^3 = 3$ since 3 is the power of e needed to give e^3. Similarly, $\ln(1/e) = \ln e^{-1} = -1$. A calculator gives $\ln 5 = 1.6094$, because $e^{1.6094} = 5$. However if we try to find $\ln(-7)$ on a calculator, we get an error message because e to any power is never negative or 0. In general

> $\ln x$ is not defined if x is negative or 0.

To work with logarithms, we use the following properties:

Properties of the Natural Logarithm

1. $\ln(AB) = \ln A + \ln B$
2. $\ln\left(\dfrac{A}{B}\right) = \ln A - \ln B$
3. $\ln(A^p) = p \ln A$
4. $\ln e^x = x$
5. $e^{\ln x} = x$

In addition, $\ln 1 = 0$ because $e^0 = 1$, and $\ln e = 1$ because $e^1 = e$.

Using the $\boxed{\text{LN}}$ button on a calculator, we get the graph of $f(x) = \ln x$ in Figure 1.63. Observe that, for large x, the graph of $y = \ln x$ climbs very slowly as x increases. The x-intercept is $x = 1$, since $\ln 1 = 0$. For $x > 1$, the value of $\ln x$ is positive; for $0 < x < 1$, the value of $\ln x$ is negative.

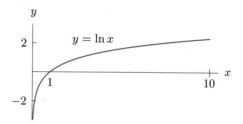

Figure 1.63: The natural logarithm function climbs very slowly

Solving Equations Using Logarithms

Natural logs can be used to solve for unknown exponents.

Example 1   Find t such that $3^t = 10$.

Solution   First, notice that we expect t to be between 2 and 3, because $3^2 = 9$ and $3^3 = 27$. To find t exactly, we take the natural logarithm of both sides and solve for t:

$$\ln(3^t) = \ln 10.$$

The third property of logarithms tells us that $\ln(3^t) = t \ln 3$, so we have

$$t \ln 3 = \ln 10$$
$$t = \frac{\ln 10}{\ln 3}.$$

Using a calculator to find the natural logs gives

$$t = 2.096.$$

Example 2   We return to the question of when the population of Nevada reaches 4 million. To get an answer, we solve $4 = 2.020(1.036)^t$ for t, using logs.

Solution   Dividing both sides of the equation by 2.020, we get

$$\frac{4}{2.020} = (1.036)^t.$$

Now take natural logs of both sides:

$$\ln\left(\frac{4}{2.020}\right) = \ln(1.036^t).$$

Using the fact that $\ln(1.036^t) = t\ln 1.036$, we get

$$\ln\left(\frac{4}{2.020}\right) = t\ln(1.036).$$

Solving this equation using a calculator to find the logs, we get

$$t = \frac{\ln(4/2.020)}{\ln(1.036)} = 19.317 \text{ years.}$$

Since $t = 0$ in 2000, this value of t corresponds to the year 2019.

Example 3   Find t such that $12 = 5e^{3t}$.

Solution   It is easiest to begin by isolating the exponential, so we divide both sides of the equation by 5:

$$2.4 = e^{3t}.$$

Now take the natural logarithm of both sides:

$$\ln 2.4 = \ln(e^{3t}).$$

Since $\ln(e^x) = x$, we have

$$\ln 2.4 = 3t,$$

so, using a calculator, we get

$$t = \frac{\ln 2.4}{3} = 0.2918.$$

Exponential Functions with Base e

An exponential function with base a has formula

$$P = P_0 a^t.$$

For any positive number a, we can write $a = e^k$ where $k = \ln a$. Thus, the exponential function can be rewritten as

$$P = P_0 a^t = P_0(e^k)^t = P_0 e^{kt}.$$

If $a > 1$, then k is positive, and if $0 < a < 1$, then k is negative. We conclude:

Writing $a = e^k$, so $k = \ln a$, any exponential function can be written in two forms

$$P = P_0 a^t \quad \text{or} \quad P = P_0 e^{kt}.$$

- If $a > 1$, we have exponential growth; if $0 < a < 1$, we have exponential decay.
- If $k > 0$, we have exponential growth; if $k < 0$, we have exponential decay.
- k is called the *continuous* growth or decay rate.

The word continuous in continuous growth rate is used in the same way to describe continuous compounding of interest earned on money. (See Appendix A.)

Example 4   (a) Convert the function $P = 1000e^{0.05t}$ to the form $P = P_0 a^t$.
(b) Convert the function $P = 500(1.06)^t$ to the form $P = P_0 e^{kt}$.

Solution   (a) Since $P = 1000e^{0.05t}$, we have $P_0 = 1000$. We want to find a so that

$$1000a^t = 1000e^{0.05t} = 1000(e^{0.05})^t.$$

We take $a = e^{0.05} = 1.0513$, so the following two functions give the same values:

$$P = 1000e^{0.05t} \quad \text{and} \quad P = 1000(1.0513)^t.$$

So a continuous growth rate of 5% is equivalent to a growth rate of 5.13% per unit time.
(b) We have $P_0 = 500$ and we want to find k with

$$500(1.06)^t = 500(e^k)^t,$$

so we take

$$1.06 = e^k$$
$$k = \ln(1.06) = 0.0583.$$

The following two functions give the same values:

$$P = 500(1.06)^t \quad \text{and} \quad P = 500e^{0.0583t}.$$

So a growth rate of 6% per unit time is equivalent to a continuous growth rate of 5.83%.

Example 5   Sketch graphs of $P = e^{0.5t}$, a continuous growth rate of 50%, and $Q = 5e^{-0.2t}$, a continuous decay rate of 20%.

Solution   The graph of $P = e^{0.5t}$ is in Figure 1.64. Notice that the graph is the same shape as the previous exponential growth curves: increasing and concave up. The graph of $Q = 5e^{-0.2t}$ is in Figure 1.65; it has the same shape as other exponential decay functions.

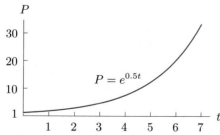

Figure 1.64: Continuous exponential growth function

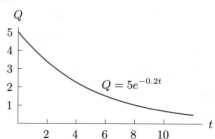

Figure 1.65: Continuous exponential decay function

Problems for Section 1.6

For Problems 1–16, solve for t using natural logarithms.

1. $5^t = 7$

2. $10 = 2^t$

3. $2 = (1.02)^t$

4. $130 = 10^t$

5. $50 = 10 \cdot 3^t$

6. $100 = 25(1.5)^t$

7. $10 = e^t$

8. $5 = 2e^t$

9. $e^{3t} = 100$

10. $10 = 6e^{0.5t}$

11. $40 = 100e^{-0.03t}$

12. $a = b^t$

13. $B = Pe^{rt}$

14. $2P = Pe^{0.3t}$

15. $5e^{3t} = 8e^{2t}$

16. $7 \cdot 3^t = 5 \cdot 2^t$

The functions in Problems 17–20 represent exponential growth or decay. What is the initial quantity? What is the growth rate? State if the growth rate is continuous.

17. $P = 5(1.07)^t$

18. $P = 7.7(0.92)^t$

19. $P = 15e^{-0.06t}$

20. $P = 3.2e^{0.03t}$

21. The following formulas give the populations of four different towns, A, B, C, and D, with t in years from now.

$$P_A = 600e^{0.08t} \qquad P_B = 1000e^{-0.02t}$$
$$P_C = 1200e^{0.03t} \qquad P_D = 900e^{0.12t}$$

    (a) Which town is growing fastest (that is, has the largest percentage growth rate)?
    (b) Which town is the largest now?
    (c) Are any of the towns decreasing in size? If so, which one(s)?

22. A city's population is 1000 and growing at 5% a year.

    (a) Find a formula for the population at time t years from now assuming that the 5% per year is an:
        (i) Annual rate   **(ii)** Continuous annual rate
    (b) In each case in part (a), estimate the population of the city in 10 years.

Write the functions in Problems 23–26 in the form $P = P_0a^t$. Which represent exponential growth and which represent exponential decay?

23. $P = 15e^{0.25t}$

24. $P = 2e^{-0.5t}$

25. $P = P_0e^{0.2t}$

26. $P = 7e^{-\pi t}$

In Problems 27–30, put the functions in the form $P = P_0e^{kt}$.

27. $P = 15(1.5)^t$

28. $P = 10(1.7)^t$

29. $P = 174(0.9)^t$

30. $P = 4(0.55)^t$

31. The population of the world can be represented by $P = 6.4(1.0126)^t$, where P is in billions of people and t is years since 2004. Find a formula for the population of the world using a continuous growth rate.

32. A fishery stocks a pond with 1000 young trout. The number of trout t years later is given by $P(t) = 1000e^{-0.5t}$.

    (a) How many trout are left after six months? After 1 year?
    (b) Find $P(3)$ and interpret it in terms of trout.
    (c) At what time are there 100 trout left?
    (d) Graph the number of trout against time, and describe how the population is changing. What might be causing this?

33. During a recession a firm's revenue declines continuously so that the revenue, R (measured in millions of dollars), in t years' time is given by $R = 5e^{-0.15t}$.

    (a) Calculate the current revenue and the revenue in two years' time.
    (b) After how many years will the revenue decline to $\$2.7$ million?

34. **(a)** What is the continuous percent growth rate for $P = 100e^{0.06t}$, with time, t, in years?
    (b) Write this function in the form $P = P_0a^t$. What is the annual percent growth rate?

35. **(a)** What is the annual percent decay rate for $P = 25(0.88)^t$, with time, t, in years?
    (b) Write this function in the form $P = P_0e^{kt}$. What is the continuous percent decay rate?

36. The gross world product is $W = 32.4(1.036)^t$, where W is in trillions of dollars and t is years since 2001. Find a formula for gross world product using a continuous growth rate.

37. The population, P, in millions, of Nicaragua was 5.4 million in 2004 and growing at an annual rate of 3.4%. Let t be time in years since 2004.

    (a) Express P as a function in the form $P = P_0a^t$.
    (b) Express P as an exponential function using base e.
    (c) Compare the annual and continuous growth rates.

38. What annual percent growth rate is equivalent to a continuous percent growth rate of 8%?

39. What continuous percent growth rate is equivalent to an annual percent growth rate of 10%?

40. The population of a city is 50,000 in 2008 and is growing at a continuous yearly rate of 4.5%.

    (a) Give the population of the city as a function of the number of years since 2008. Sketch a graph of the population against time.
    (b) What will be the city's population in the year 2018?
    (c) Calculate the time for the population of the city to reach 100,000. This is called the doubling time of the population.

41. In 2000, there were about 213 million vehicles (cars and trucks) and about 281 million people in the US. The number of vehicles has been growing at 4% a year, while the population has been growing at 1% a year. If the growth rates remain constant, when is there, on average, one vehicle per person?

1.7 EXPONENTIAL GROWTH AND DECAY

Many quantities in nature change according to an exponential growth or decay function of the form $P = P_0 e^{kt}$, where P_0 is the initial quantity and k is the continuous growth or decay rate.

Example 1 The Environmental Protection Agency (EPA) recently investigated a spill of radioactive iodine. The radiation level at the site was about 2.4 millirems/hour (four times the maximum acceptable limit of 0.6 millirems/hour), so the EPA ordered an evacuation of the surrounding area. The level of radiation from an iodine source decays at a continuous hourly rate of $k = -0.004$.

(a) What was the level of radiation 24 hours later?

(b) Find the number of hours until the level of radiation reached the maximum acceptable limit, and the inhabitants could return.

Solution

(a) The level of radiation, R, in millirems/hour, at time t, in hours since the initial measurement, is given by
$$R = 2.4e^{-0.004t},$$
so the level of radiation 24 hours later was
$$R = 2.4e^{(-0.004)(24)} = 2.18 \text{ millirems per hour.}$$

(b) A graph of $R = 2.4e^{-0.004t}$ is in Figure 1.66. The maximum acceptable value of R is 0.6 millirems per hour, which occurs at approximately $t = 350$. Using logarithms, we have
$$0.6 = 2.4e^{-0.004t}$$
$$0.25 = e^{-0.004t}$$
$$\ln 0.25 = -0.004t$$
$$t = \frac{\ln 0.25}{-0.004} = 346.57.$$

The inhabitants will not be able to return for 346.57 hours, or about 15 days.

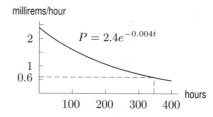

Figure 1.66: The level of radiation from radioactive iodine

Example 2 The population of Kenya[56] was 19.5 million in 1984 and 39.0 million in 2009. Assuming the population increases exponentially, find a formula for the population of Kenya as a function of time.

Solution We measure the population, P, in millions and time, t, in years since 1984. We can express P in terms of t using the continuous growth rate k by
$$P = P_0 e^{kt} = 19.5e^{kt},$$
where $P_0 = 19.5$ is the initial value of P. We find k using the fact that $P = 39.0$ when $t = 25$:
$$39.0 = 19.5e^{k \cdot 25}.$$

Divide both sides by 19.5, giving
$$\frac{39.0}{19.5} = e^{25k}.$$

[56]www.cia.gov/library/publications/the-world-factbook.

Take natural logs of both sides:

$$\ln\left(\frac{39.0}{19.5}\right) = \ln(e^{25k}).$$

Since $\ln(e^{25k}) = 25k$, this becomes

$$\ln\left(\frac{39.0}{19.5}\right) = 25k.$$

We get

$$k = \frac{1}{25}\ln\left(\frac{39.0}{19.5}\right) = 0.028,$$

and therefore

$$P = 19.5e^{0.028t}.$$

Since $k = 0.028 = 2.8\%$, the population of Kenya was growing at a continuous rate of 2.8% per year.

Doubling Time and Half-Life

Every exponential growth function has a constant doubling time and every exponential decay function has a constant half-life.

> The **doubling time** of an exponentially increasing quantity is the time required for the quantity to double.
> The **half-life** of an exponentially decaying quantity is the time required for the quantity to be reduced by a factor of one half.

Example 3   Show algebraically that every exponentially growing function has a fixed doubling time.

Solution   Consider the exponential function $P = P_0 a^t$. For any base a with $a > 1$, there is a positive number d such that $a^d = 2$. We show that d is the doubling time. If the population is P at time t, then at time $t + d$, the population is

$$P_0 a^{t+d} = P_0 a^t a^d = (P_0 a^t)(2) = 2P.$$

So, no matter what the initial quantity and no matter what the initial time, the size of the population is doubled d time units later.

Example 4   The release of chlorofluorocarbons used in air conditioners and household sprays (hair spray, shaving cream, etc.) destroys the ozone in the upper atmosphere. The quantity of ozone, Q, is decaying exponentially at a continuous rate of 0.25% per year. What is the half-life of ozone? In other words, at this rate, how long will it take for half the ozone to disappear?

Solution   If Q_0 is the initial quantity of ozone and t is in years, then

$$Q = Q_0 e^{-0.0025t}.$$

We want to find the value of t making $Q = Q_0/2$, so

$$\frac{Q_0}{2} = Q_0 e^{-0.0025t}.$$

Dividing both sides by Q_0 and taking natural logs gives

$$\ln\left(\frac{1}{2}\right) = -0.0025t,$$

so

$$t = \frac{\ln(1/2)}{-0.0025} = 277 \text{ years}.$$

Half the present atmospheric ozone will be gone in 277 years.

Financial Applications: Compound Interest

We deposit $100 in a bank paying interest at a rate of 8% per year. How much is in the account at the end of the year? This depends on how often the interest is compounded. If the interest is paid into the account *annually*, that is, only at the end of the year, then the balance in the account after one year is $108. However, if the interest is paid twice a year, then 4% is paid at the end of the first six months and 4% at the end of the year. Slightly more money is earned this way, since the interest paid early in the year will earn interest during the rest of the year. This effect is called *compounding*.

In general, the more often interest is compounded, the more money is earned (although the increase may not be large). What happens if interest is compounded more frequently, such as every minute or every second? The benefit of increasing the frequency of compounding becomes negligible beyond a certain point. When that point is reached, we find the balance using the number e and we say that the interest per year is *compounded continuously*. If we have deposited $100 in an account paying 8% interest per year compounded continuously, the balance after one year is $100e^{0.08} = \$108.33$. Compounding is discussed further in Appendix B. In general:

An amount P_0 is deposited in an account paying interest at a rate of r per year. Let P be the balance in the account after t years.
- If interest is compounded annually, then $P = P_0(1+r)^t$.
- If interest is compounded continuously, then $P = P_0e^{rt}$, where $e = 2.71828....$

We write P_0 for the initial deposit because it is the value of P when $t = 0$. Note that for a 7% interest rate, $r = 0.07$. If a rate is continuous, we will say so explicitly.

Example 5   A bank advertises an interest rate of 8% per year. If you deposit $5000, how much is in the account 3 years later if the interest is compounded (a) Annually?   (b) Continuously?

Solution   (a) For annual compounding, $P = P_0(1+r)^t = 5000(1.08)^3 = \$6298.56$.
(b) For continuous compounding, $P = P_0e^{rt} = 5000e^{0.08 \cdot 3} = \$6356.25$. As expected, the amount in the account 3 years later is larger if the interest is compounded continuously ($6356.25) than if the interest is compounded annually ($6298.56).

Example 6   If $10,000 is deposited in an account paying interest at a rate of 5% per year, compounded continuously, how long does it take for the balance in the account to reach $15,000?

Solution   Since interest is compounded continuously, we use $P = P_0e^{rt}$ with $r = 0.05$ and $P_0 = 10,000$. We want to find the value of t for which $P = 15,000$. The equation is

$$15,000 = 10,000e^{0.05t}.$$

Now divide both sides by 10,000, then take logarithms and solve for t:

$$1.5 = e^{0.05t}$$
$$\ln(1.5) = \ln(e^{0.05t})$$
$$\ln(1.5) = 0.05t$$
$$t = \frac{\ln(1.5)}{0.05} = 8.1093.$$

It takes about 8.1 years for the balance in the account to reach $15,000.

Example 7   (a) Calculate the doubling time, D, for interest rates of 2%, 3%, 4%, and 5% per year, compounded annually.

(b) Use your answers to part (a) to check that an interest rate of i% gives a doubling time approximated for small values of i by

$$D \approx \frac{70}{i} \text{ years.}$$

This is the "Rule of 70" used by bankers: To compute the approximate doubling time of an investment, divide 70 by the percent annual interest rate.

Solution   (a) We find the doubling time for an interest rate of 2% per year using the formula $P = P_0(1.02)^t$ with t in years. To find the value of t for which $P = 2P_0$, we solve

$$2P_0 = P_0(1.02)^t$$
$$2 = (1.02)^t$$
$$\ln 2 = \ln(1.02)^t$$
$$\ln 2 = t\ln(1.02) \quad \text{(using the third property of logarithms)}$$
$$t = \frac{\ln 2}{\ln 1.02} = 35.003 \text{ years.}$$

With an annual interest rate of 2%, it takes about 35 years for an investment to double in value. Similarly, we find the doubling times for 3%, 4%, and 5% in Table 1.33.

Table 1.33   *Doubling time as a function of interest rate*

i (% annual growth rate)	2	3	4	5
D (doubling time in years)	35.003	23.450	17.673	14.207

(b) We compute $(70/i)$ for $i = 2, 3, 4, 5$. The results are shown in Table 1.34.

Table 1.34   *Approximate doubling time as a function of interest rate: Rule of 70*

i (% annual growth rate)	2	3	4	5
$(70/i)$ (Approximate doubling time in years)	35.000	23.333	17.500	14.000

Comparing Tables 1.33 and 1.34, we see that the quantity $(70/i)$ gives a reasonably accurate approximation to the doubling time, D, for the small interest rates we considered.

Present and Future Value

Many business deals involve payments in the future. For example, when a car is bought on credit, payments are made over a period of time. Being paid $100 in the future is clearly worse than being paid $100 today for many reasons. If we are given the money today, we can do something else with it—for example, put it in the bank, invest it somewhere, or spend it. Thus, even without considering inflation, if we are to accept payment in the future, we would expect to be paid more to compensate for this loss of potential earnings.[57] The question we consider now is, how much more?

To simplify matters, we consider only what we would lose by not earning interest; we do not consider the effect of inflation. Let's look at some specific numbers. Suppose we deposit $100 in an account that earns 7% interest per year compounded annually, so that in a year's time we have $107. Thus, $100 today is worth $107 a year from now. We say that the $107 is the *future value* of the $100, and that the $100 is the *present value* of the $107. In general, we say the following:

---
[57]This is referred to as the time value of money.

- The **future value**, B, of a payment, P, is the amount to which the P would have grown if deposited today in an interest-bearing bank account.
- The **present value**, P, of a future payment, B, is the amount that would have to be deposited in a bank account today to produce exactly B in the account at the relevant time in the future.

Due to the interest earned, the future value is larger than the present value. The relation between the present and future values depends on the interest rate, as follows.

Suppose B is the *future value* of P and P is the *present value* of B.
If interest is compounded annually at a rate r for t years, then

$$B = P(1 + r)^t, \quad \text{or equivalently,} \quad P = \frac{B}{(1 + r)^t}.$$

If interest is compounded continuously at a rate r for t years, then

$$B = Pe^{rt}, \quad \text{or equivalently,} \quad P = \frac{B}{e^{rt}} = Be^{-rt}.$$

The rate, r, is sometimes called the *discount rate*. The present value is often denoted by PV and the future value by FV.

Example 8 You win the lottery and are offered the choice between $1 million in four yearly installments of $250,000 each, starting now, and a lump-sum payment of $920,000 now. Assuming a 6% interest rate per year, compounded continuously, and ignoring taxes, which should you choose?

Solution We assume that you pick the option with the largest present value. The first of the four $250,000 payments is made now, so

$$\text{Present value of first payment} = \$250{,}000.$$

The second payment is made one year from now and so

$$\text{Present value of second payment} = \$250{,}000e^{-0.06(1)}.$$

Calculating the present value of the third and fourth payments similarly, we find:

$$\text{Total present value} = \$250{,}000 + \$250{,}000e^{-0.06(1)} + \$250{,}000e^{-0.06(2)} + \$250{,}000e^{-0.06(3)}$$
$$= \$250{,}000 + \$235{,}441 + \$221{,}730 + \$208{,}818$$
$$= \$915{,}989.$$

Since the present value of the four payments is less than $920,000, you are better off taking the $920,000 now.

Alternatively, we can compare the future values of the two pay schemes. We calculate the future value of both schemes three years from now, on the date of the last $250,000 payment. At that time,

$$\text{Future value of the lump-sum payment} = \$920{,}000e^{0.06(3)} = \$1{,}101{,}440.$$

The future value of the first $250,000 payment is $250{,}000e^{0.06(3)}$. Calculating the future value of the other payments similarly, we find:

$$\text{Total future value} = \$250{,}000e^{0.06(3)} + \$250{,}000e^{0.06(2)} + \$250{,}000e^{0.06(1)} + \$250{,}000$$
$$= \$299{,}304 + \$281{,}874 + \$265{,}459 + \$250{,}000$$
$$= \$1{,}096{,}637.$$

As we expect, the future value of the $920,000 payment is greater, so you are better off taking the $920,000 now.[58]

Problems for Section 1.7

1. World wind energy generating[59] capacity, W, was 18,000 megawatts in 2000 and has been increasing at a continuous rate of approximately 27% per year. Assume this rate continues.

   (a) Give a formula for W, in megawatts, as a function of time, t, in years since 2000.
   (b) When is wind capacity predicted to pass 250,000 megawatts?

2. The half-life of nicotine in the blood is 2 hours. A person absorbs 0.4 mg of nicotine by smoking a cigarette. Fill in the following table with the amount of nicotine remaining in the blood after t hours. Estimate the length of time until the amount of nicotine is reduced to 0.04 mg.

t (hours)	0	2	4	6	8	10
Nicotine (mg)	0.4					

3. If you deposit $10,000 in an account earning interest at an 8% annual rate compounded continuously, how much money is in the account after five years?

4. If you need $20,000 in your bank account in 6 years, how much must be deposited now? The interest rate is 10%, compounded continuously.

5. If a bank pays 6% per year interest compounded continuously, how long does it take for the balance in an account to double?

6. Suppose $1000 is invested in an account paying interest at a rate of 5.5% per year. How much is in the account after 8 years if the interest is compounded

   (a) Annually?   (b) Continuously?

7. Find the doubling time of a quantity that is increasing by 7% per year.

8. If $12,000 is deposited in an account paying 8% interest per year, compounded continuously, how long will it take for the balance to reach $20,000?

9. You want to invest money for your child's education in a certificate of deposit (CD). You want it to be worth $12,000 in 10 years. How much should you invest if the CD pays interest at a 9% annual rate compounded
   (a) Annually?   (b) Continuously?

10. From October 2002 to October 2006 the number $N(t)$ of Wikipedia articles was approximated by $N(t) =$ $N_0 e^{t/500}$, where t is the number of days after October 1, 2002. Find the doubling time for the number of Wikipedia articles during this period.

11. A cup of coffee contains 100 mg of caffeine, which leaves the body at a continuous rate of 17% per hour.

    (a) Write a formula for the amount, A mg, of caffeine in the body t hours after drinking a cup of coffee.
    (b) Graph the function from part (a). Use the graph to estimate the half-life of caffeine.
    (c) Use logarithms to find the half-life of caffeine.

12. A population, currently 200, is growing at 5% per year.

    (a) Write a formula for the population, P, as a function of time, t, years in the future.
    (b) Graph P against t.
    (c) Estimate the population 10 years from now.
    (d) Use the graph to estimate the doubling time of the population.

13. Figure 1.67 shows the balances in two bank accounts. Both accounts pay the same interest rate, but one compounds continuously and the other compounds annually. Which curve corresponds to which compounding method? What is the initial deposit in each case?

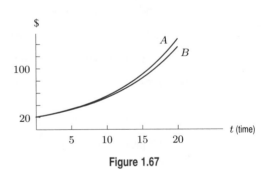

Figure 1.67

14. The exponential function $y(x) = Ce^{\alpha x}$ satisfies the conditions $y(0) = 2$ and $y(1) = 1$. Find the constants C and α. What is $y(2)$?

---

[58]If you read the fine print, you will find that many lotteries do not make their payments right away, but often spread them out, sometimes far into the future. This is to reduce the present value of the payments made, so that the value of the prizes is less than it might first appear!

[59]World Wind Energy Association, www.wwindea.org, accessed September 6, 2009.

15. Air pressure, P, decreases exponentially with the height, h, in meters above sea level:

$$P = P_0 e^{-0.00012h}$$

where P_0 is the air pressure at sea level.

(a) At the top of Mount McKinley, height 6194 meters (about 20,320 feet), what is the air pressure, as a percent of the pressure at sea level?

(b) The maximum cruising altitude of an ordinary commercial jet is around 12,000 meters (about 39,000 feet). At that height, what is the air pressure, as a percent of the sea level value?

16. The antidepressant fluoxetine (or Prozac) has a half-life of about 3 days. What percentage of a dose remains in the body after one day? After one week?

17. A firm decides to increase output at a constant relative rate from its current level of 20,000 to 30,000 units during the next five years. Calculate the annual percent rate of increase required to achieve this growth.

18. The half-life of a radioactive substance is 12 days. There are 10.32 grams initially.

(a) Write an equation for the amount, A, of the substance as a function of time.

(b) When is the substance reduced to 1 gram?

19. One of the main contaminants of a nuclear accident, such as that at Chernobyl, is strontium-90, which decays exponentially at a rate of approximately 2.5% per year.

(a) Write the percent of strontium-90 remaining, P, as a function of years, t, since the nuclear accident. [Hint: 100% of the contaminant remains at $t = 0$.]

(b) Graph P against t.

(c) Estimate the half-life of strontium-90.

(d) After the Chernobyl disaster, it was predicted that the region would not be safe for human habitation for 100 years. Estimate the percent of original strontium-90 remaining at this time.

20. The number of people living with HIV infections increased worldwide approximately exponentially from 2.5 million in 1985 to 37.8 million in 2003.[60] (HIV is the virus that causes AIDS.)

(a) Give a formula for the number of HIV infections, H, (in millions) as a function of years, t, since 1985. Use the form $H = H_0 e^{kt}$. Graph this function.

(b) What was the yearly continuous percent change in the number of HIV infections between 1985 and 2003?

21. (a) Figure 1.68 shows exponential growth. Starting at $t = 0$, estimate the time for the population to double.

(b) Repeat part (a), but this time start at $t = 3$.

(c) Pick any other value of t for the starting point, and notice that the doubling time is the same no matter where you start.

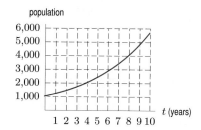

Figure 1.68

22. An exponentially growing animal population numbers 500 at time $t = 0$; two years later, it is 1500. Find a formula for the size of the population in t years and find the size of the population at $t = 5$.

23. If the quantity of a substance decreases by 4% in 10 hours, find its half-life.

24. Pregnant women metabolize some drugs at a slower rate than the rest of the population. The half-life of caffeine is about 4 hours for most people. In pregnant women, it is 10 hours.[61] (This is important because caffeine, like all psychoactive drugs, crosses the placenta to the fetus.) If a pregnant woman and her husband each have a cup of coffee containing 100 mg of caffeine at 8 am, how much caffeine does each have left in the body at 10 pm?

25. The half-life of radioactive strontium-90 is 29 years. In 1960, radioactive strontium-90 was released into the atmosphere during testing of nuclear weapons, and was absorbed into people's bones. How many years does it take until only 10% of the original amount absorbed remains?

26. In 1923, koalas were introduced on Kangaroo Island off the coast of Australia. In 1996, the population was 5000. By 2005, the population had grown to 27,000, prompting a debate on how to control their growth and avoid koalas dying of starvation.[62] Assuming exponential growth, find the (continuous) rate of growth of the koala population between 1996 and 2005. Find a formula for the population as a function of the number of years since 1996, and estimate the population in the year 2020.

27. The total world marine catch in 1950 was 17 million tons and in 2001 was 99 million tons.[63] If the marine catch is increasing exponentially, find the (continuous) rate of increase. Use it to predict the total world marine catch in the year 2020.

---

[60] *The World Almanac and Book of Facts 2005*, p. 89 (New York).

[61] From Robert M. Julien, *A Primer of Drug Action*, 7th ed., p. 159 (New York: W. H. Freeman, 1995).

[62] news.yahoo.com/s/afp/australiaanimalskoalas, accessed June 1, 2005.

[63] *The World Almanac and Book of Facts 2005*, p. 143 (New York).

28. (a) Use the Rule of 70 to predict the doubling time of an investment which is earning 8% interest per year.

(b) Find the doubling time exactly, and compare your answer to part (a).

29. The island of Manhattan was sold for $24 in 1626. Suppose the money had been invested in an account which compounded interest continuously.

(a) How much money would be in the account in the year 2005 if the yearly interest rate was

(i) 5%?   (ii) 7%?

(b) If the yearly interest rate was 6%, in what year would the account be worth one million dollars?

30. In 2004, the world's population was 6.4 billion, and the population was projected to reach 8.5 billion by the year 2030. What annual growth rate is projected?

31. A picture supposedly painted by Vermeer (1632–1675) contains 99.5% of its carbon-14 (half-life 5730 years). From this information decide whether the picture is a fake. Explain your reasoning.

32. Find the future value in 8 years of a $10,000 payment today, if the interest rate is 3% per year compounded continuously.

33. Find the future value in 15 years of a $20,000 payment today, if the interest rate is 3.8% per year compounded continuously.

34. Find the present value of an $8000 payment to be made in 5 years. The interest rate is 4% per year compounded continuously.

35. Find the present value of a $20,000 payment to be made in 10 years. Assume an interest rate of 3.2% per year compounded continuously.

36. Interest is compounded annually. Consider the following choices of payments to you:

Choice 1: $1500 now and $3000 one year from now

Choice 2: $1900 now and $2500 one year from now

(a) If the interest rate on savings were 5% per year, which would you prefer?

(b) Is there an interest rate that would lead you to make a different choice? Explain.

37. A person is to be paid $2000 for work done over a year. Three payment options are being considered. Option 1 is to pay the $2000 in full now. Option 2 is to pay $1000 now and $1000 in a year. Option 3 is to pay the full $2000 in a year. Assume an annual interest rate of 5% a year, compounded continuously.

(a) Without doing any calculations, which option is the best option financially for the worker? Explain.

(b) Find the future value, in one year's time, of all three options.

(c) Find the present value of all three options.

38. A business associate who owes you $3000 offers to pay you $2800 now, or else pay you three yearly installments of $1000 each, with the first installment paid now. If you use only financial reasons to make your decision, which option should you choose? Justify your answer, assuming a 6% interest rate per year, compounded continuously.

39. Big Tree McGee is negotiating his rookie contract with a professional basketball team. They have agreed to a three-year deal which will pay Big Tree a fixed amount at the end of each of the three years, plus a signing bonus at the beginning of his first year. They are still haggling about the amounts and Big Tree must decide between a big signing bonus and fixed payments per year, or a smaller bonus with payments increasing each year. The two options are summarized in the table. All values are payments in millions of dollars.

	Signing bonus	Year 1	Year 2	Year 3
Option #1	6.0	2.0	2.0	2.0
Option #2	1.0	2.0	4.0	6.0

(a) Big Tree decides to invest all income in stock funds which he expects to grow at a rate of 10% per year, compounded continuously. He would like to choose the contract option which gives him the greater future value at the end of the three years when the last payment is made. Which option should he choose?

(b) Calculate the present value of each contract offer.

40. A company is considering whether to buy a new machine, which costs $97,000. The cash flows (adjusted for taxes and depreciation) that would be generated by the new machine are given in the following table:

Year	1	2	3	4
Cash flow	$50,000	$40,000	$25,000	$20,000

(a) Find the total present value of the cash flows. Treat each year's cash flow as a lump sum at the end of the year and use an interest rate of 7.5% per year, compounded annually.

(b) Based on a comparison of the cost of the machine and the present value of the cash flows, would you recommend purchasing the machine?

41. You win $38,000 in the state lottery to be paid in two installments—$19,000 now and $19,000 one year from now. A friend offers you $36,000 in return for your two lottery payments. Instead of accepting your friend's offer, you take out a one-year loan at an interest rate of 8.25% per year, compounded annually. The loan will be paid back by a single payment of $19,000 (your second lottery check) at the end of the year. Which is better, your friend's offer or the loan?

42. You are considering whether to buy or lease a machine whose purchase price is \$12,000. Taxes on the machine will be \$580 due in one year, \$464 due in two years, and \$290 due in three years. If you buy the machine, you expect to be able to sell it after three years for \$5,000. If you lease the machine for three years, you make an initial payment of \$2650 and then three payments of \$2650 at the end of each of the next three years. The leasing company will pay the taxes. The interest rate is 7.75% per year, compounded annually. Should you buy or lease the machine? Explain.

43. You are buying a car that comes with a one-year warranty and are considering whether to purchase an extended warranty for \$375. The extended warranty covers the two years immediately after the one-year warranty expires. You estimate that the yearly expenses that would have been covered by the extended warranty are \$150 at the end of the first year of the extension and \$250 at the end of the second year of the extension. The interest rate is 5% per year, compounded annually. Should you buy the extended warranty? Explain.

1.8 NEW FUNCTIONS FROM OLD

We have studied linear and exponential functions, and the logarithm function. In this section, we learn how to create new functions by composing, stretching, and shifting functions we already know.

Composite Functions

A drop of water falls onto a paper towel. The area, A of the circular damp spot is a function of r, its radius, which is a function of time, t. We know $A = f(r) = \pi r^2$; suppose $r = g(t) = t + 1$. By substitution, we express A as a function of t:

$$A = f(g(t)) = \pi(t+1)^2.$$

The function $f(g(t))$ is a "function of a function," or a *composite function*, in which there is an *inside function* and an *outside function*. To find $f(g(2))$, we first add one ($g(2) = 2 + 1 = 3$) and then square and multiply by π. We have

$$f(g(2)) = \pi(2+1)^2 \; = \; \pi 3^2 \; = \; 9\pi.$$

First calculation   Second calculation

The inside function is $t + 1$ and the outside function is squaring and multiplying by π. In general, the inside function represents the calculation that is done first and the outside function represents the calculation done second.

Example 1 If $f(t) = t^2$ and $g(t) = t + 2$, find
(a) $f(t+1)$ (b) $f(t) + 3$ (c) $f(t+h)$ (d) $f(g(t))$ (e) $g(f(t))$

Solution
(a) Since $t + 1$ is the inside function, $f(t + 1) = (t + 1)^2$.
(b) Here 3 is added to $f(t)$, so $f(t) + 3 = t^2 + 3$.
(c) Since $t + h$ is the inside function, $f(t + h) = (t + h)^2$.
(d) Since $g(t) = t + 2$, substituting $t + 2$ into f gives $f(g(t)) = f(t + 2) = (t + 2)^2$.
(e) Since $f(t) = t^2$, substituting t^2 into g gives $g(f(t)) = g(t^2) = t^2 + 2$.

Example 2 If $f(x) = e^x$ and $g(x) = 5x + 1$, find (a) $f(g(x))$ (b) $g(f(x))$

Solution
(a) Substituting $g(x) = 5x + 1$ into f gives $f(g(x)) = f(5x + 1) = e^{5x+1}$.
(b) Substituting $f(x) = e^x$ into g gives $g(f(x)) = g(e^x) = 5e^x + 1$.

Example 3 Using the following table, find $g(f(0))$, $f(g(0))$, $f(g(1))$, and $g(f(1))$.

x	0	1	2	3
$f(x)$	3	1	-1	-3
$g(x)$	0	2	4	6

Solution   To find $g(f(0))$, we first find $f(0) = 3$ from the table. Then we have $g(f(0)) = g(3) = 6$.
For $f(g(0))$, we must find $g(0)$ first. Since $g(0) = 0$, we have $f(g(0)) = f(0) = 3$.
Similar reasoning leads to $f(g(1)) = f(2) = -1$ and $g(f(1)) = g(1) = 2$.

We can write a composite function using a new variable u to represent the value of the inside function. For example

$$y = (t+1)^4 \qquad \text{is the same as} \qquad y = u^4 \quad \text{with} \quad u = t+1.$$

Other expressions for u, such as $u = (t+1)^2$, with $y = u^2$, are also possible.

Example 4   Use a new variable u for the inside function to express each of the following as a composite function:
(a) $y = \ln(3t)$ (b) $w = 5(2r+3)^2$ (c) $P = e^{-0.03t}$

Solution   (a) We take the inside function to be $3t$, so $y = \ln u$ with $u = 3t$.
(b) We take the inside function to be $2r + 3$, so $w = 5u^2$ with $u = 2r + 3$.
(c) We take the inside function to be $-0.03t$, so $P = e^u$ with $u = -0.03t$.

Stretches of Graphs

If the demand function is linear, the graph of a possible revenue function $R = f(p)$ is in Figure 1.69. What does the graph of $R = 3f(p)$ look like? The factor 3 in the function $R = 3f(p)$ stretches each $f(p)$ revenue value by multiplying it by 3. See Figure 1.70. If c is positive, the graph of $R = cf(p)$ is the graph of $R = f(p)$ stretched or shrunk vertically by c units. If c is negative, the function no longer makes sense as a revenue function, but we can still draw the graph. What does the graph of $R = -2f(p)$ look like? The factor -2 in the function $R = -2f(p)$ stretches $f(p)$ by multiplying by 2 and reflecting it about the x-axis. See Figure 1.70.

Multiplying a function by a constant, c, stretches the graph vertically (if $c > 1$) or shrinks the graph vertically (if $0 < c < 1$). A negative sign (if $c < 0$) reflects the graph about the x-axis, in addition to shrinking or stretching.

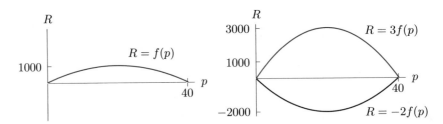

Figure 1.69: Graph of $f(p)$ Figure 1.70: Multiples of the function $f(p)$

Shifted Graphs

Consider the function $y = x^2 + 4$. The y-coordinates for this function are exactly 4 units larger than the corresponding y-coordinates of the function $y = x^2$. So the graph of $y = x^2 + 4$ is obtained from the graph of $y = x^2$ by adding 4 to the y-coordinate of each point; that is, by moving the graph of $y = x^2$ up 4 units. (See Figure 1.71.)

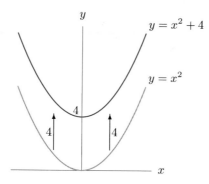

Figure 1.71: Vertical shift: Graphs of
$y = x^2$ and $y = x^2 + 4$

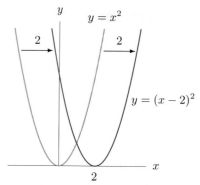

Figure 1.72: Horizontal shift: Graphs of
$y = x^2$ and $y = (x - 2)^2$

A graph can also be shifted to the left or to the right. In Figure 1.72, we see that the graph of $y = (x - 2)^2$ is the graph of $y = x^2$ shifted to the right 2 units. In general,

- The graph of $y = f(x) + k$ is the graph of $y = f(x)$ moved up k units (down if k is negative).
- The graph of $y = f(x - k)$ is the graph of $y = f(x)$ moved to the right k units (to the left if k is negative).

Example 5   (a) A cost function, $C(q)$, for a company is shown in Figure 1.73. The fixed cost increases by $1000. Sketch a graph of the new cost function.

(b) A supply curve, S, for a product is given in Figure 1.74. A new factory opens and produces 100 units of the product no matter what the price. Sketch a graph of the new supply curve.

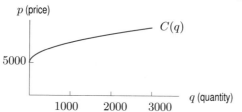

Figure 1.73: A cost function

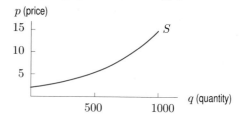

Figure 1.74: A supply function

Solution   (a) For each quantity, the new cost is $1000 more than the old cost. The new cost function is $C(q) + 1000$, whose graph is the graph of $C(q)$ shifted vertically up 1000 units. (See Figure 1.75.)

(b) To see the effect of the new factory, look at an example. At a price of 10 dollars, approximately 800 units are currently produced. With the new factory, this amount increases by 100 units, so the new amount produced is 900 units. At each price, the quantity produced increases by 100, so the new supply curve is S shifted horizontally to the right by 100 units. (See Figure 1.76.)

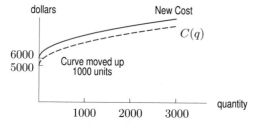

Figure 1.75: New cost function (original curve dashed)

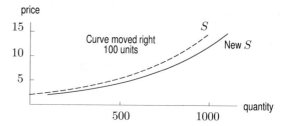

Figure 1.76: New supply curve (original curve dashed)

Problems for Section 1.8

1. For $g(x) = x^2 + 2x + 3$, find and simplify:

(a) $g(2 + h)$ (b) $g(2)$

(c) $g(2 + h) - g(2)$

2. If $f(x) = x^2 + 1$, find and simplify:

(a) $f(t + 1)$ (b) $f(t^2 + 1)$ (c) $f(2)$

(d) $2f(t)$ (e) $[f(t)]^2 + 1$

For the functions f and g in Problems 3–6, find

(a) $f(g(1))$ (b) $g(f(1))$ (c) $f(g(x))$

(d) $g(f(x))$ (e) $f(t)g(t)$

3. $f(x) = x^2$, $g(x) = x + 1$

4. $f(x) = \sqrt{x + 4}$, $g(x) = x^2$

5. $f(x) = e^x$, $g(x) = x^2$

6. $f(x) = 1/x$, $g(x) = 3x + 4$

7. Let $f(x) = x^2$ and $g(x) = 3x - 1$. Find the following:

(a) $f(2) + g(2)$ (b) $f(2) \cdot g(2)$

(c) $f(g(2))$ (d) $g(f(2))$

In Problems 8–10, find the following:

(a) $f(g(x))$ (b) $g(f(x))$ (c) $f(f(x))$

8. $f(x) = 2x^2$ and $g(x) = x + 3$

9. $f(x) = 2x + 3$ and $g(x) = 5x^2$

10. $f(x) = x^2 + 1$ and $g(x) = \ln x$

11. Use Table 1.35 to find:

(a) $f(g(0))$ (b) $f(g(1))$ (c) $f(g(2))$

(d) $g(f(2))$ (e) $g(f(3))$

Table 1.35

x	0	1	2	3	4	5
$f(x)$	10	6	3	4	7	11
$g(x)$	2	3	5	8	12	15

12. Make a table of values for each of the following functions using Table 1.35:

(a) $f(x) + 3$ (b) $f(x - 2)$ (c) $5g(x)$

(d) $-f(x) + 2$ (e) $g(x - 3)$ (f) $f(x) + g(x)$

13. Use the variable u for the inside function to express each of the following as a composite function:

(a) $y = 2^{3x-1}$ (b) $P = \sqrt{5t^2 + 10}$

(c) $w = 2\ln(3r + 4)$

14. Use the variable u for the inside function to express each of the following as a composite function:

(a) $y = (5t^2 - 2)^6$ (b) $P = 12e^{-0.6t}$

(c) $C = 12\ln(q^3 + 1)$

Simplify the quantities in Problems 15–18 using $m(z) = z^2$.

15. $m(z + 1) - m(z)$ **16.** $m(z + h) - m(z)$

17. $m(z) - m(z - h)$ **18.** $m(z + h) - m(z - h)$

For Problems 19–21, use the graphs in Figure 1.77.

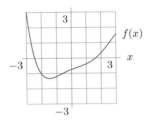 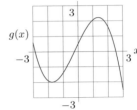

Figure 1.77

19. Estimate $f(g(1))$.   **20.** Estimate $g(f(2))$.

21. Estimate $f(f(1))$.

22. Using Table 1.36, create a table of values for $f(g(x))$ and for $g(f(x))$.

Table 1.36

x	-3	-2	-1	0	1	2	3
$f(x)$	0	1	2	3	2	1	0
$g(x)$	3	2	2	0	-2	-2	-3

23. A tree of height y meters has, on average, B branches, where $B = y - 1$. Each branch has, on average, n leaves where $n = 2B^2 - B$. Find the average number of leaves of a tree as a function of height.

In Problems 24–27, use Figure 1.78 to estimate the function value or explain why it cannot be done.

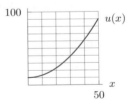 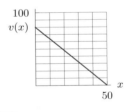

Figure 1.78

24. $u(v(10))$ **25.** $u(v(40))$

26. $v(u(10))$ **27.** $v(u(40))$

28. The Heaviside step function, H, is graphed in Figure 1.79. Graph the following functions.

(a) $2H(x)$ (b) $H(x) + 1$ (c) $H(x+1)$
(d) $-H(x)$ (e) $H(-x)$

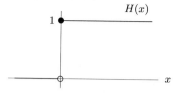

Figure 1.79

For the functions f in Exercises 29–31, graph:

(a) $f(x+2)$ (b) $f(x-1)$ (c) $f(x) - 4$
(d) $f(x+1) + 3$ (e) $3f(x)$ (f) $-f(x) + 1$

29.

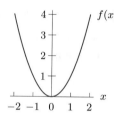

30.

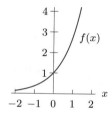

31.

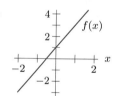

Graph the functions in Problems 32–37 using Figure 1.80.

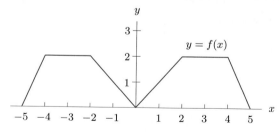

Figure 1.80

32. $y = f(x) + 2$

33. $y = 2f(x)$

34. $y = f(x-1)$

35. $y = -3f(x)$

36. $y = 2f(x) - 1$

37. $y = 2 - f(x)$

For the functions $f(x)$ in Problems 38–41, graph:

(a) $y = f(x) + 2$ (b) $y = f(x-1)$
(c) $y = 3f(x)$ (d) $y = -f(x)$

38.

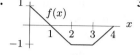

39.

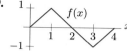

40.

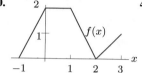

41.

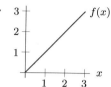

42. Morphine, a pain-relieving drug, is administered to a patient intravenously starting at 8 am. The drug saturation curve $Q = f(t)$ in Figure 1.81 gives the quantity, Q, of morphine in the blood t hours after 8 am.

(a) Draw the drug saturation curve $Q = g(t)$ if the IV line is started at noon instead of 8 am.
(b) Is g one of the following transformations of f: vertical shift, vertical stretch, horizontal shift, horizontal stretch? If so, which?
(c) Write $g(t)$ in terms of the function f.

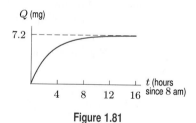

Figure 1.81

43. (a) Write an equation for a graph obtained by vertically stretching the graph of $y = x^2$ by a factor of 2, followed by a vertical upward shift of 1 unit. Sketch it.
(b) What is the equation if the order of the transformations (stretching and shifting) in part (a) is interchanged?
(c) Are the two graphs the same? Explain the effect of reversing the order of transformations.

1.9 PROPORTIONALITY AND POWER FUNCTIONS

Proportionality

A common functional relationship occurs when one quantity is *proportional* to another. For example, if apples are $1.40 a pound, we say the price you pay, p dollars, is proportional to the weight you buy, w pounds, because

$$p = f(w) = 1.40w.$$

As another example, the area, A, of a circle is proportional to the square of the radius, r:

$$A = f(r) = \pi r^2.$$

> We say y is (directly) **proportional** to x if there is a nonzero constant k such that
>
> $$y = kx.$$
>
> This k is called the constant of proportionality.

We also say that one quantity is *inversely proportional* to another if one is proportional to the reciprocal of the other. For example, the speed, v, at which you make a 50-mile trip is inversely proportional to the time, t, taken, because v is proportional to $1/t$:

$$v = 50 \left(\frac{1}{t} \right) = \frac{50}{t}.$$

Notice that if y is directly proportional to x, then the magnitude of one variable increases (decreases) when the magnitude of the other increases (decreases). If, however, y is inversely proportional to x, then the magnitude of one variable increases when the magnitude of the other decreases.

Example 1   The heart mass of a mammal is proportional to its body mass.[64]

(a) Write a formula for heart mass, H, as a function of body mass, B.
(b) A human with a body mass of 70 kilograms has a heart mass of 0.42 kilograms. Use this information to find the constant of proportionality.
(c) Estimate the heart mass of a horse with a body mass of 650 kg.

Solution   (a) Since H is proportional to B, for some constant k, we have

$$H = kB.$$

(b) We use the fact that $H = 0.42$ when $B = 70$ to solve for k:

$$H = kB$$
$$0.42 = k(70)$$
$$k = \frac{0.42}{70} = 0.006.$$

(c) Since $k = 0.006$, we have $H = 0.006B$, so the heart mass of the horse is given by

$$H = 0.006(650) = 3.9 \text{ kilograms.}$$

---

[64] K. Schmidt-Nielson: *Scaling—Why is Animal Size So Important?* (Cambridge: CUP, 1984).

Example 2   The period of a pendulum, T, is the amount of time required for the pendulum to make one complete swing. For small swings, the period, T, is approximately proportional to the square root of l, the pendulum's length. So

$$T = k\sqrt{l} \quad \text{where } k \text{ is a constant.}$$

Notice that T is not directly proportional to l, but T is proportional to $\sqrt{l}$.

Example 3   An object's weight, w, is inversely proportional to the square of its distance, r, from the earth's center. So, for some constant k,

$$w = \frac{k}{r^2}.$$

Here w is not inversely proportional to r, but to r^2.

Power Functions

In each of the previous examples, one quantity is proportional to the power of another quantity. We make the following definition:

> We say that $Q(x)$ is a **power function** of x if $Q(x)$ is proportional to a constant power of x. If k is the constant of proportionality, and if p is the power, then
>
> $$Q(x) = k \cdot x^p.$$

For example, the function $H = 0.006B$ is a power function with $p = 1$. The function $T = k\sqrt{l} = kl^{1/2}$ is a power function with $p = 1/2$, and the function $w = k/r^2 = kr^{-2}$ is a power function with $p = -2$.

Example 4   Which of the following are power functions? For those which are, write the function in the form $y = kx^p$, and give the coefficient k and the exponent p.

(a) $\quad y = \dfrac{5}{x^3}$ 　　　　　(b) $\quad y = \dfrac{2}{3x}$ 　　　　　(c) $\quad y = \dfrac{5x^2}{2}$

(d) $\quad y = 5 \cdot 2^x$ 　　　　　(e) $\quad y = 3\sqrt{x}$ 　　　　　(f) $\quad y = (3x^2)^3$

Solution

(a) Since $y = 5x^{-3}$, this is a power function with $k = 5$ and $p = -3$.
(b) Since $y = (2/3)x^{-1}$, this is a power function with $k = 2/3$ and $p = -1$.
(c) Since $y = (5/2)x^2$, this is a power function with $k = 5/2 = 2.5$ and $p = 2$.
(d) This is not a power function. It is an exponential function.
(e) Since $y = 3x^{1/2}$, this is a power function with $k = 3$ and $p = 1/2$.
(f) Since $y = 3^3 \cdot (x^2)^3 = 27x^6$, this is a power function with $k = 27$ and $p = 6$.

Graphs of Power Functions

The graph of $y = x^2$ is shown in Figure 1.82. It is decreasing for negative x and increasing for positive x. Notice that it is bending upward, or concave up, for all x. The graph of $y = x^3$ is shown in Figure 1.83. Notice that it is bending downward, or concave down for negative x and bending upward, or concave up for positive x. The graph of $y = \sqrt{x} = x^{1/2}$ is shown in Figure 1.84. Notice that the graph is increasing and concave down.

Since x^2 increases without bound as x increases, we often say that it tends to infinity as x approaches infinity, which we write in symbols as

$$x^2 \to \infty \quad \text{as} \quad x \to \infty.$$

Since x^3 decreases without bound as x decreases, we write

$$x^3 \to -\infty \quad \text{as} \quad x \to -\infty.$$

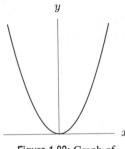

Figure 1.82: Graph of
$y = x^2$

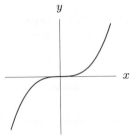

Figure 1.83: Graph of
$y = x^3$

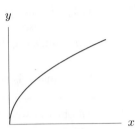

Figure 1.84: Graph of
$y = x^{1/2}$

Example 5   If N is the average number of species found on an island and A is the area of the island, observations have shown[65] that N is approximately proportional to the cube root of A. Write a formula for N as a function of A and describe the shape of the graph of this function.

Solution   For some positive constant k, we have

$$N = k \sqrt[3]{A} = kA^{1/3}.$$

It turns out that the value of k depends on the region of the world in which the island is found. The graph of N against A (for $A > 0$) has a shape similar to the graph in Figure 1.84. It is increasing and concave down. Thus, larger islands have more species on them (as we would expect), but the increase slows as the island gets larger.

The function $y = x^0 = 1$ has a graph that is a horizontal line. For negative powers, rewriting

$$y = x^{-1} = \frac{1}{x} \quad \text{and} \quad y = x^{-2} = \frac{1}{x^2}$$

makes it clear that as $x > 0$ increases, the denominators increase and the functions decrease. The graphs of $y = x^{-1}$ and $y = x^{-2}$ have both the x- and y-axes as asymptotes. (See Figure 1.85.)

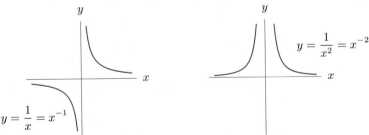

$y = \frac{1}{x} = x^{-1}$

$y = \frac{1}{x^2} = x^{-2}$

Figure 1.85: Graphs of x^0 and of negative powers of x

Quadratic Functions and Polynomials

Sums of power functions with nonnegative integer exponents are called *polynomials*, which are functions of the form

$$y = p(x) = a_n x^n + a_{n-1} x^{n-1} + \cdots + a_1 x + a_0.$$

Here, n is a nonnegative integer, called the *degree* of the polynomial, and a_n is a nonzero number called the *leading coefficient*. We call $a_n x^n$ the *leading term*.

If $n = 2$, the polynomial is called *quadratic* and has the form $ax^2 + bx + c$ with $a \neq 0$. The graph of a quadratic polynomial is a parabola. It opens up if the leading coefficient a is positive and opens down if a is negative.

[65] *Scientific American*, p. 112 (September, 1989).

Example 6   A company finds that the average number of people attending a concert is 75 if the price is $50 per person. At a price of $35 per person, the average number of people in attendance is 120.

(a) Assume that the demand curve is a line. Write the demand, q, as a function of price, p.
(b) Use your answer to part (a) to write the revenue, R, as a function of price, p.
(c) Use a graph of the revenue function to determine what price should be charged to obtain the greatest revenue.

Solution   (a) Two points on the line are $(p, q) = (50, 75)$ and $(p, q) = (35, 120)$. The slope of the line is

$$m = \frac{120 - 75}{35 - 50} = \frac{45}{-15} = -3 \text{ people/dollar.}$$

To find the vertical intercept of the line, we use the slope and one of the points:

$$75 = b + (-3)(50)$$
$$225 = b$$

The demand function is $q = 225 - 3p$.

(b) Since $R = pq$ and $q = 225 - 3p$, we see that $R = p(225 - 3p) = 225p - 3p^2$.
(c) The revenue function is the quadratic polynomial graphed in Figure 1.86. The maximum revenue occurs at $p = 37.5$. Thus, the company maximizes revenue by charging $37.50 per person.

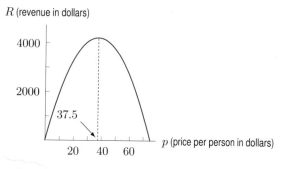

Figure 1.86: Revenue function for concert ticket sales

Problems for Section 1.9

In Problems 1–12, determine whether or not the function is a power function. If it is a power function, write it in the form $y = kx^p$ and give the values of k and p.

1. $y = 5\sqrt{x}$ **2.** $y = \dfrac{3}{x^2}$ **3.** $y = 2^x$

4. $y = \dfrac{3}{8x}$ **5.** $y = (3x^5)^2$ **6.** $y = \dfrac{5}{2\sqrt{x}}$

7. $y = 3 \cdot 5^x$ **8.** $y = \dfrac{2x^2}{10}$ **9.** $y = \dfrac{8}{x}$

10. $y = (5x)^3$ **11.** $y = 3x^2 + 4$ **12.** $y = \dfrac{x}{5}$

In Problems 13–16, write a formula representing the function.

13. The strength, S, of a beam is proportional to the square of its thickness, h.

14. The energy, E, expended by a swimming dolphin is proportional to the cube of the speed, v, of the dolphin.

15. The average velocity, v, for a trip over a fixed distance, d, is inversely proportional to the time of travel, t.

16. The gravitational force, F, between two bodies is inversely proportional to the square of the distance d between them.

17. The number of species of lizards, N, found on an island off Baja California is proportional to the fourth root of the area, A, of the island.[66] Write a formula for N as a function of A. Graph this function. Is it increasing or decreasing? Is the graph concave up or concave down? What does this tell you about lizards and island area?

18. The surface area of a mammal, S, satisfies the equation $S = kM^{2/3}$, where M is the body mass, and the constant of proportionality k depends on the body shape of the mammal. A human of body mass 70 kilograms has surface area 18,600 cm^2. Find the constant of proportionality for humans. Find the surface area of a human with body mass 60 kilograms.

19. Use shifts of power functions to find a possible formula for each of the graphs:

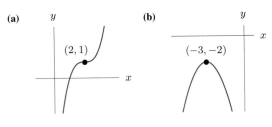

(a)

(b)

20. Kleiber's Law states that the metabolic needs (such as calorie requirements) of a mammal are proportional to its body weight raised to the 0.75 power.[67] Surprisingly, the daily diets of mammals conform to this relation well. Assuming Kleiber's Law holds:

(a) Write a formula for C, daily calorie consumption, as a function of body weight, W.
(b) Sketch a graph of this function. (You do not need scales on the axes.)
(c) If a human weighing 150 pounds needs to consume 1800 calories a day, estimate the daily calorie requirement of a horse weighing 700 lbs and of a rabbit weighing 9 lbs.
(d) On a per-pound basis, which animal requires more calories: a mouse or an elephant?

21. Allometry is the study of the relative size of different parts of a body as a consequence of growth. In this problem, you will check the accuracy of an allometric equation: the weight of a fish is proportional to the cube of its length.[68] Table 1.37 relates the weight, y, in gm, of plaice (a type of fish) to its length, x, in cm. Does this data support the hypothesis that (approximately) $y = kx^3$? If so, estimate the constant of proportionality, k.

Table 1.37

x	y	x	y	x	y
33.5	332	37.5	455	41.5	623
34.5	363	38.5	500	42.5	674
35.5	391	39.5	538	43.5	724
36.5	419	40.5	574		

22. The blood mass of a mammal is proportional to its body mass. A rhinoceros with body mass 3000 kilograms has blood mass of 150 kilograms. Find a formula for the blood mass of a mammal as a function of the body mass and estimate the blood mass of a human with body mass 70 kilograms.

23. Biologists estimate that the number of animal species of a certain body length is inversely proportional to the square of the body length.[69] Write a formula for the number of animal species, N, of a certain body length as a function of the length, L. Are there more species at large lengths or at small lengths? Explain.

24. The specific heat, s, of an element is the number of calories of heat required to raise the temperature of one gram of the element by one degree Celsius. Use the following table to decide if s is proportional or inversely proportional to the atomic weight, w, of the element. If so, find the constant of proportionality.

Element	Li	Mg	Al	Fe	Ag	Pb	Hg
w	6.9	24.3	27.0	55.8	107.9	207.2	200.6
s	0.92	0.25	0.21	0.11	0.056	0.031	.033

25. The circulation time of a mammal (that is, the average time it takes for all the blood in the body to circulate once and return to the heart) is proportional to the fourth root of the body mass of the mammal.

(a) Write a formula for the circulation time, T, in terms of the body mass, B.
(b) If an elephant of body mass 5230 kilograms has a circulation time of 148 seconds, find the constant of proportionality.
(c) What is the circulation time of a human with body mass 70 kilograms?

[66]Rosenzweig, M.L., *Species Diversity in Space and Time*, p. 143 (Cambridge: Cambridge University Press, 1995).

[67]Strogatz, S., "Math and the City", The New York Times, May 20, 2009. Kleiber originally estimated the exponent as 0.74; it is now believed to be 0.75.

[68]Adapted from "On the Dynamics of Exploited Fish Populations" by R. J. H. Beverton and S. J. Holt, *Fishery Investigations*, Series II, 19, 1957.

[69]*US News & World Report*, August 18, 1997, p. 79.

Table 1.39

r	8	9	10	11	12
m	31.447	34.484	37.611	40.814	44.084

26. The DuBois formula relates a person's surface area s, in m^2, to weight w, in kg, and height h, in cm, by

$$s = 0.01w^{0.25}h^{0.75}.$$

(a) What is the surface area of a person who weighs 65 kg and is 160 cm tall?
(b) What is the weight of a person whose height is 180 cm and who has a surface area of 1.5 m^2?
(c) For people of fixed weight 70 kg, solve for h as a function of s. Simplify your answer.

27. The infrastructure needs of a region (for example, the number of miles of electrical cable, the number of miles of roads, the number of gas stations) depend on its population. Cities enjoy economies of scale.[70] For example, the number of gas stations is proportional to the population raised to the power of 0.77.

(a) Write a formula for the number, N, of gas stations in a city as a function of the population, P, of the city.
(b) If city A is 10 times bigger than city B, how do their number of gas stations compare?
(c) Which is expected to have more gas stations per person, a town of 10,000 people or a city of 500,000 people?

28. According to the National Association of Realtors,[71] the minimum annual gross income, m, in thousands of dollars, needed to obtain a 30-year home loan of A thousand dollars at 9% is given in Table 1.38. Note that the larger the loan, the greater the income needed. Of course, not every mortgage is financed at 9%. In fact, excepting for slight variations, mortgage interest rates are generally determined not by individual banks but by the economy as a whole. The minimum annual gross income, m, in thousands of dollars, needed for a home loan of $100,000 at various interest rates, r, is given in Table 1.39. Note that obtaining a loan at a time when interest rates are high requires a larger income.

(a) Is the size of the loan, A, proportional to the minimum annual gross income, m?
(b) Is the percentage rate, r, proportional to the minimum annual gross income, m?

Table 1.38

A	50	75	100	150	200
m	17.242	25.863	34.484	51.726	68.968

29. A standard tone of 20,000 dynes/cm^2 (about the loudness of a rock band) is assigned a value of 10. A subject listened to other sounds, such as a light whisper, normal conversation, thunder, a jet plane at takeoff, and so on. In each case, the subject was asked to judge the loudness and assign it a number relative to 10, the value of the standard tone. This is a "judgment of magnitude" experiment. The power law $J = al^{0.3}$ was found to model the situation well, where l is the actual loudness (measured in dynes/cm^2) and J is the judged loudness.

(a) What is the value of a?
(b) What is the judged loudness if the actual loudness is 0.2 dynes/cm^2 (normal conversation)?
(c) What is the actual loudness if judged loudness is 20?

30. A sporting goods wholesaler finds that when the price of a product is $25, the company sells 500 units per week. When the price is $30, the number sold per week decreases to 460 units.

(a) Find the demand, q, as a function of price, p, assuming that the demand curve is linear.
(b) Use your answer to part (a) to write revenue as a function of price.
(c) Graph the revenue function in part (b). Find the price that maximizes revenue. What is the revenue at this price?

31. A health club has cost and revenue functions given by $C = 10,000 + 35q$ and $R = pq$, where q is the number of annual club members and p is the price of a one-year membership. The demand function for the club is $q = 3000 - 20p$.

(a) Use the demand function to write cost and revenue as functions of p.
(b) Graph cost and revenue as a function of p, on the same axes. (Note that price does not go above $170 and that the annual costs of running the club reach $120,000.)
(c) Explain why the graph of the revenue function has the shape it does.
(d) For what prices does the club make a profit?
(e) Estimate the annual membership fee that maximizes profit. Mark this point on your graph.

[70]Strogatz, S., "Math and the City", *The New York Times*, May 20, 2009.
[71]"Income Needed to Get a Mortgage," *The World Almanac 1992*, p. 720.

1.10 PERIODIC FUNCTIONS

What Are Periodic Functions?

Many functions have graphs that oscillate, resembling a wave. Figure 1.87 shows the number of new housing construction starts (one-family units) in the US, 2002–2005, where t is time in quarter-years.[72] Notice that few new homes begin construction during the first quarter of a year (January, February, and March), whereas many new homes are begun in the second quarter (April, May, and June). Since 2008, as the economy has slowed, the pattern of oscillations has been replaced by a sharp drop in housing construction.

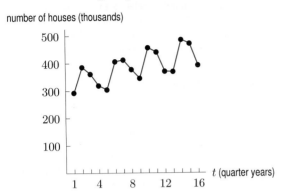

Figure 1.87: New housing construction starts, 2002–2005

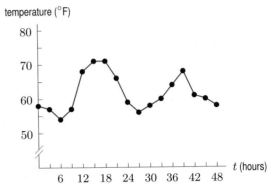

Figure 1.88: Temperature in Phoenix after midnight February 17, 2005

Let's look at another example. Figure 1.88 is a graph of the temperature (in °F) in Phoenix, AZ, in hours after midnight, February 17, 2005. Notice that the maximum is in the afternoon and the minimum is in the early morning.[73] Again, the graph looks like a wave.

Functions whose values repeat at regular intervals are called *periodic*. Many processes, such as the number of housing starts or the temperature, are approximately periodic. The water level in a tidal basin, the blood pressure in a heart, retail sales in the US, and the position of air molecules transmitting a musical note are also all periodic functions of time.

Amplitude and Period

Periodic functions repeat exactly the same cycle forever. If we know one cycle of the graph, we know the entire graph.

> For any periodic function of time:
> - The **amplitude** is half the difference between its maximum and minimum values.
> - The **period** is the time for the function to execute one complete cycle.

Example 1   Estimate the amplitude and period of the new housing starts function shown in Figure 1.87.

Solution   Figure 1.87 is not exactly periodic, since the maximum and minimum are not the same for each cycle. Nonetheless, the minimum is about 300, and the maximum is about 450. The difference between them is 150, so the amplitude is about $\frac{1}{2}(150) = 75$ thousand houses.

The wave completes a cycle between $t = 1$ and $t = 5$, so the period is $t = 4$ quarter-years, or one year. The business cycle for new housing construction is one year.

---

[72]http://www.census.gov/const/www/quarterly_starts_completions.pdf, accessed May 25, 2009.
[73]http://www.weather.com, accessed February 20, 2005.

Example 2   Figure 1.89 shows the temperature in an unopened freezer. Estimate the temperature in the freezer at 12:30 and at 2:45.

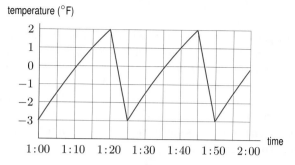

Figure 1.89: Oscillating freezer temperature. Estimate the temperature at 12:30 and 2:45

Solution   The maximum and minimum values each occur every 25 minutes, so the period is 25 minutes. The temperature at 12:30 should be the same as at 12:55 and at 1:20, namely, 2°F. Similarly, the temperature at 2:45 should be the same as at 2:20 and 1:55, or about -1.5°F.

The Sine and Cosine

Many periodic functions are represented using the functions called *sine* and *cosine*. The keys for the sine and cosine on a calculator are usually labeled as $\boxed{\text{sin}}$ and $\boxed{\text{cos}}$.

Warning: Your calculator can be in either "degree" mode or "radian" mode. For this book, always use "radian" mode.

Graphs of the Sine and Cosine

The graphs of the sine and the cosine functions are periodic; see Figures 1.90 and 1.91. Notice that the graph of the cosine function is the graph of the sine function, shifted $\pi/2$ to the left.

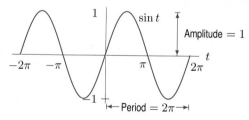

Figure 1.90: Graph of $\sin t$

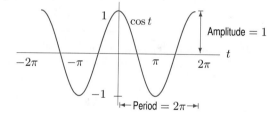

Figure 1.91: Graph of $\cos t$

The maximum and minimum values of $\sin t$ are $+1$ and -1, so the amplitude of the sine function is 1. The graph of $y = \sin t$ completes a cycle between $t = 0$ and $t = 2\pi$; the rest of the graph repeats this portion. The period of the sine function is 2π.

Example 3   Use a graph of $y = 3\sin 2t$ to estimate the amplitude and period of this function.

Solution   In Figure 1.92, the waves have a maximum of $+3$ and a minimum of -3, so the amplitude is 3. The graph completes one complete cycle between $t = 0$ and $t = \pi$, so the period is π.

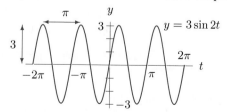

Figure 1.92: The amplitude is 3 and the period is π

Example 4   Explain how the graphs of each of the following functions differ from the graph of $y = \sin t$.

(a) $y = 6 \sin t$ (b) $y = 5 + \sin t$ (c) $y = \sin(t + \frac{\pi}{2})$

Solution   (a) The graph of $y = 6 \sin t$ is in Figure 1.93. The maximum and minimum values are $+6$ and -6, so the amplitude is 6. This is the graph of $y = \sin t$ stretched vertically by a factor of 6.

(b) The graph of $y = 5 + \sin t$ is in Figure 1.94. The maximum and minimum values of this function are 6 and 4, so the amplitude is $(6 - 4)/2 = 1$. The amplitude (or size of the wave) is the same as for $y = \sin t$, since this is a graph of $y = \sin t$ shifted up 5 units.

(c) The graph of $y = \sin(t + \frac{\pi}{2})$ is in Figure 1.95. This has the same amplitude, namely 1, and period, namely 2π, as the graph of $y = \sin t$. It is the graph of $y = \sin t$ shifted $\pi/2$ units to the left. (In fact, this is the graph of $y = \cos t$.)

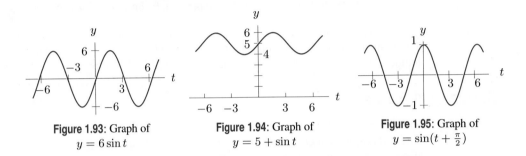

Figure 1.93: Graph of   Figure 1.94: Graph of   Figure 1.95: Graph of
$y = 6 \sin t$ $y = 5 + \sin t$ $y = \sin(t + \frac{\pi}{2})$

Families of Curves: The Graph of $y = A \sin(Bt)$

The constants A and B in the expression $y = A \sin(Bt)$ are called *parameters*. We can study families of curves by varying one parameter at a time and studying the result.

Example 5   (a) Graph $y = A \sin t$ for several positive values of A. Describe the effect of A on the graph.
(b) Graph $y = \sin(Bt)$ for several positive values of B. Describe the effect of B on the graph.

Solution   (a) From the graphs of $y = A \sin t$ for $A = 1, 2, 3$ in Figure 1.96, we see that A is the amplitude.

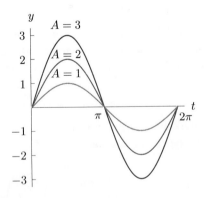

Figure 1.96: Graphs of $y = A \sin t$ with $A = 1, 2, 3$

(b) The graphs of $y = \sin(Bt)$ for $B = \frac{1}{2}, B = 1$, and $B = 2$ are shown in Figure 1.97. When $B = 1$, the period is 2π; when $B = 2$, the period is π; and when $B = \frac{1}{2}$, the period is 4π.

The parameter B affects the period of the function. The graphs suggest that the larger B is, the shorter the period. In fact, the period is $2\pi/B$.

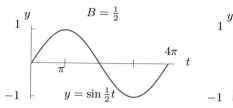

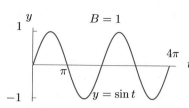

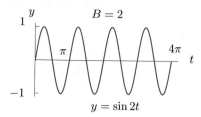

Figure 1.97: Graphs of $y = \sin(Bt)$ with $B = \frac{1}{2}, 1, 2$

In Example 5, the amplitude of $y = A\sin(Bt)$ was determined by the parameter A, and the period was determined by the parameter B. In general, we have

> The functions $y = A\sin(Bt) + C$ and $y = A\cos(Bt) + C$ are periodic with
>
> $$\text{Amplitude} = |A|, \qquad \text{Period} = \frac{2\pi}{|B|}, \qquad \text{Vertical shift} = C$$

Example 6   Find possible formulas for the following periodic functions.

(a)
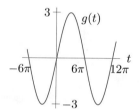

(b)
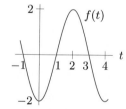

(c)
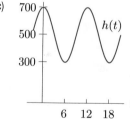

Solution

(a) This function looks like a sine function of amplitude 3, so $g(t) = 3\sin(Bt)$. Since the function executes one full oscillation between $t = 0$ and $t = 12\pi$, when t changes by 12π, the quantity Bt changes by 2π. This means $B \cdot 12\pi = 2\pi$, so $B = 1/6$. Therefore, $g(t) = 3\sin(t/6)$ has the graph shown.

(b) This function looks like an upside-down cosine function with amplitude 2, so $f(t) = -2\cos(Bt)$. The function completes one oscillation between $t = 0$ and $t = 4$. Thus, when t changes by 4, the quantity Bt changes by 2π, so $B \cdot 4 = 2\pi$, or $B = \pi/2$. Therefore, $f(t) = -2\cos(\pi t/2)$ has the graph shown.

(c) This function looks like a cosine function. The maximum is 700 and the minimum is 300, so the amplitude is $\frac{1}{2}(700 - 300) = 200$. The height halfway between the maximum and minimum is 500, so the cosine curve has been shifted up 500 units, so $h(t) = 500 + 200\cos(Bt)$. The period is 12, so $B \cdot 12 = 2\pi$. Thus, $B = \pi/6$. The function $h(t) = 500 + 200\cos(\pi t/6)$ has the graph shown.

Example 7   On June 23, 2009, high tide in Portland, Maine was at midnight.[74] The height of the water in the harbor is a periodic function, since it oscillates between high and low tide. If t is in hours since midnight, the height (in feet) is approximated by the formula

$$y = 4.9 + 4.4 \cos\left(\frac{\pi}{6}t\right).$$

(a) Graph this function from $t = 0$ to $t = 24$.
(b) What was the water level at high tide?
(c) When was low tide, and what was the water level at that time?
(d) What is the period of this function, and what does it represent in terms of tides?
(e) What is the amplitude of this function, and what does it represent in terms of tides?

Solution   (a) See Figure 1.98.
(b) The water level at high tide was 9.3 feet (given by the y-intercept on the graph).
(c) Low tide occurs at $t = 6$ (6 am) and at $t = 18$ (6 pm). The water level at this time is 0.5 feet.
(d) The period is 12 hours and represents the interval between successive high tides or successive low tides. Of course, there is something wrong with the assumption in the model that the period is 12 hours. If so, the high tide would always be at noon or midnight, instead of progressing slowly through the day, as it in fact does. The interval between successive high tides actually averages about 12 hours 39 minutes, which could be taken into account in a more precise mathematical model.
(e) The maximum is 9.3, and the minimum is 0.5, so the amplitude is $(9.3 - 0.5)/2$, which is 4.4 feet. This represents half the difference between the depths at high and low tide.

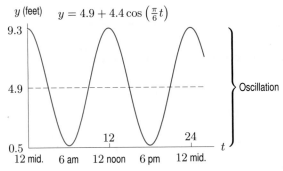

Figure 1.98: Graph of the function approximating the depth of the water in Portland, Maine on June 23, 2009

Problems for Section 1.10

1. A graduate student in environmental science studied the temperature fluctuations of a river. Figure 1.99 shows the temperature of the river (in °C) every hour, with hour 0 being midnight of the first day.

   (a) Explain why a periodic function could be used to model these data.
   (b) Approximately when does the maximum occur? The minimum? Why does this make sense?
   (c) What is the period for these data? What is the amplitude?

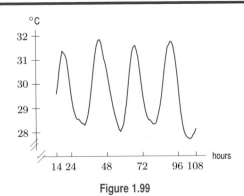

Figure 1.99

---

[74]www.maineboats.com/tidecharts/tides?T=junpt09.

2. Figure 1.100 shows quarterly beer production during the period 1997 to 1999. Quarter 1 reflects production during the first three months of the year, etc.[75]

    (a) Explain why a periodic function should be used to model these data.

    (b) Approximately when does the maximum occur? The minimum? Why does this make sense?

    (c) What are the period and amplitude for these data?

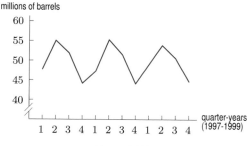

millions of barrels

quarter-years
(1997-1999)

Figure 1.100

3. Sketch a possible graph of sales of sunscreen in the northeastern US over a 3-year period, as a function of months since January 1 of the first year. Explain why your graph should be periodic. What is the period?

For Problems 4–9, sketch graphs of the functions. What are their amplitudes and periods?

    4. $y = 3\sin x$

    5. $y = 3\sin 2x$

    6. $y = -3\sin 2\theta$

    7. $y = 4\cos 2x$

    8. $y = 4\cos(\frac{1}{2}t)$

    9. $y = 5 - \sin 2t$

10. Values of a function are given in the following table. Explain why this function appears to be periodic. Approximately what are the period and amplitude of the function? Assuming that the function is periodic, estimate its value at $t = 15$, at $t = 75$, and at $t = 135$.

t	20	25	30	35	40	45	50	55	60
$f(t)$	1.8	1.4	1.7	2.3	2.0	1.8	1.4	1.7	2.3

11. The following table shows values of a periodic function $f(x)$. The maximum value attained by the function is 5.

    (a) What is the amplitude of this function?

    (b) What is the period of this function?

    (c) Find a formula for this periodic function.

x	0	2	4	6	8	10	12
$f(x)$	5	0	-5	0	5	0	-5

12. Figure 1.101 shows the levels of the hormones estrogen and progesterone during the monthly ovarian cycles in females.[76] Is the level of both hormones periodic? What is the period in each case? Approximately when in the monthly cycle is estrogen at a peak? Approximately when in the monthly cycle is progesterone at a peak?

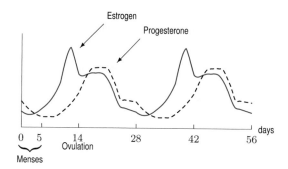

Figure 1.101

13. Average daily high temperatures in Ottawa, the capital of Canada, range from a low of $-6°$ Celsius on January 1 to a high of $26°$ Celsius on July 1 six months later. See Figure 1.102. Find a formula for H, the average daily high temperature in Ottawa in, $°C$, as a function of t, the number of months since January 1.

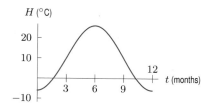

Figure 1.102

14. A person breathes in and out every three seconds. The volume of air in the person's lungs varies between a minimum of 2 liters and a maximum of 4 liters. Which of the following is the best formula for the volume of air in the person's lungs as a function of time?

    (a) $y = 2 + 2\sin\left(\frac{\pi}{3}t\right)$
    (b) $y = 3 + \sin\left(\frac{2\pi}{3}t\right)$

    (c) $y = 2 + 2\sin\left(\frac{2\pi}{3}t\right)$
    (d) $y = 3 + \sin\left(\frac{\pi}{3}t\right)$

---

[75] www.beerinstitute.org/pdfs/PRODUCTION_AND_WITHDRAWALS_OF_MALT_BEVERAGES_1997_1999.pdf, accessed May 7, 2005.

[76] Robert M. Julien, *A Primer of Drug Action*, Seventh Edition, p. 360 (W. H. Freeman and Co., New York: 1995).

15. Delta Cephei is one of the most visible stars in the night sky. Its brightness has periods of 5.4 days, the average brightness is 4.0 and its brightness varies by ± 0.35. Find a formula that models the brightness of Delta Cephei as a function of time, t, with $t = 0$ at peak brightness.

16. Most breeding birds in the northeast US migrate elsewhere during the winter. The number of bird species in an Ohio forest preserve oscillates between a high of 28 in June and a low of 10 in December.[77]

   (a) Graph the number of bird species in this preserve as a function of t, the number of months since June. Include at least three years on your graph.
   (b) What are the amplitude and period of this function?
   (c) Find a formula for the number of bird species, B, as a function of the number of months, t since June.

For Problems 17–28, find a possible formula for each graph.

17.

18.

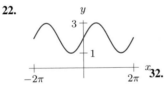

19.

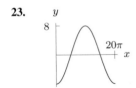

20.

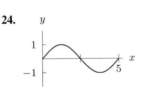

21.

22.

23.

24.

25.

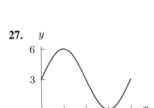

26.

27.

28.

29. The depth of water in a tank oscillates once every 6 hours. If the smallest depth is 5.5 feet and the largest depth is 8.5 feet, find a possible formula for the depth in terms of time in hours.

30. The desert temperature, H, oscillates daily between $40°$F at 5 am and $80°$F at 5 pm. Write a possible formula for H in terms of t, measured in hours from 5 am.

31. Table 1.40 gives values for $g(t)$, a periodic function.

   (a) Estimate the period and amplitude for this function.
   (b) Estimate $g(34)$ and $g(60)$.

Table 1.40

t	0	2	4	6	8	10	12	14
$g(t)$	14	19	17	15	13	11	14	19
t	16	18	20	22	24	26	28	
$g(t)$	17	15	13	11	14	19	17	

32. The Bay of Fundy in Canada has the largest tides in the world. The difference between low and high water levels is 15 meters (nearly 50 feet). At a particular point the depth of the water, y meters, is given as a function of time, t, in hours since midnight by

$$y = D + A\cos\left(B(t - C)\right).$$

   (a) What is the physical meaning of D?
   (b) What is the value of A?
   (c) What is the value of B? Assume the time between successive high tides is 12.4 hours.
   (d) What is the physical meaning of C?

[77]Rosenzweig, M.L., *Species Diversity in Space and Time*, p. 71 (Cambridge University Press, 1995).

CHAPTER SUMMARY

- **Function terminology**
  Domain/range, increasing/decreasing, concavity, intercepts.

- **Linear functions**
  Slope, y-intercept. Grow by equal amounts in equal times.

- **Economic applications**
  Cost, revenue, and profit functions, break-even point. Supply and demand curves, equilibrium point. Depreciation function. Budget constraint. Present and future value.

- **Change, average rate of change, relative change**

- **Exponential functions**
  Exponential growth and decay, growth rate, the number e, continuous growth rate, doubling time, half-life, compound interest. Grow by equal percentages in equal times.

- **The natural logarithm function**

- **New functions from old**
  Composition, shifting, stretching.

- **Power functions and proportionality**

- **Polynomials**

- **Periodic functions**
  Sine, cosine, amplitude, period.

REVIEW PROBLEMS FOR CHAPTER ONE

1. The time T, in minutes, that it takes Dan to run x kilometers is a function $T = f(x)$. Explain the meaning of the statement $f(5) = 23$ in terms of running.

2. Describe what Figure 1.103 tells you about an assembly line whose productivity is represented as a function of the number of workers on the line.

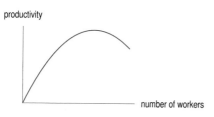

Figure 1.103

3. It warmed up throughout the morning, and then suddenly got much cooler around noon, when a storm came through. After the storm, it warmed up before cooling off at sunset. Sketch temperature as a function of time.

4. A gas tank 6 meters underground springs a leak. Gas seeps out and contaminates the soil around it. Graph the amount of contamination as a function of the depth (in meters) below ground.

5. The yield, Y, of an apple orchard (in bushels) as a function of the amount, a, of fertilizer (in pounds) used on the orchard is shown in Figure 1.104.

   (a) Describe the effect of the amount of fertilizer on the yield of the orchard.
   (b) What is the vertical intercept? Explain what it means in terms of apples and fertilizer.
   (c) What is the horizontal intercept? Explain what it means in terms of apples and fertilizer.
   (d) What is the range of this function for $0 \le a \le 80$?
   (e) Is the function increasing or decreasing at $a = 60$?

   (f) Is the graph concave up or down near $a = 40$?

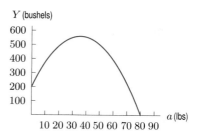

Figure 1.104

6. Let $y = f(x) = 3x - 5$.

   (a) What is $f(1)$?
   (b) Find the value of y when x is 5.
   (c) Find the value of x when y is 4.
   (d) Find the average rate of change of f between $x = 2$ and $x = 4$.

7. You drive at a constant speed from Chicago to Detroit, a distance of 275 miles. About 120 miles from Chicago you pass through Kalamazoo, Michigan. Sketch a graph of your distance from Kalamazoo as a function of time.

Find the equation of the line passing through the points in Problems 8–11.

8. $(0, -1)$ and $(2, 3)$

9. $(-1, 3)$ and $(2, 2)$

10. $(0, 2)$ and $(2, 2)$

11. $(-1, 3)$ and $(-1, 4)$

12. Match the graphs in Figure 1.105 with the following equations. (Note that the x and y scales may be unequal.)

(a) $y = x - 5$

(b) $-3x + 4 = y$

(c) $5 = y$

(d) $y = -4x - 5$

(e) $y = x + 6$

(f) $y = x/2$

(I) y

(II) y

(III) y

(IV) y

(V) y

(VI) y

Figure 1.105

13. Find a linear function that generates the values in Table 1.41.

Table 1.41

x	5.2	5.3	5.4	5.5	5.6
y	27.8	29.2	30.6	32.0	33.4

14. A controversial 1992 Danish study[78] reported that men's average sperm count has decreased from 113 million per milliliter in 1940 to 66 million per milliliter in 1990.

(a) Express the average sperm count, S, as a linear function of the number of years, t, since 1940.

(b) A man's fertility is affected if his sperm count drops below about 20 million per milliliter. If the linear model found in part (a) is accurate, in what year will the average male sperm count fall below this level?

15. Residents of the town of Maple Grove who are connected to the municipal water supply are billed a fixed amount monthly plus a charge for each cubic foot of water used. A household using 1000 cubic feet was billed \$40, while one using 1600 cubic feet was billed \$55.

(a) What is the charge per cubic foot?

(b) Write an equation for the total cost of a resident's water as a function of cubic feet of water used.

(c) How many cubic feet of water used would lead to a bill of \$100?

In Problems 16–21, find the average velocity for the position function $s(t)$, in mm, over the interval $1 \le t \le 3$, where t is in seconds.

16. $s(t) = 12t - t^2$

17. $s(t) = \ln(t)$

18.

t	0	1	2	3
$s(t)$	7	3	7	11

19.

t	0	1	2	3
$s(t)$	8	4	2	4

20.
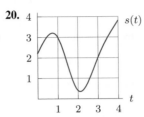

21.
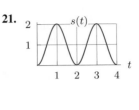

22. The graphs in Figure 1.106 represent the temperature, H, of four loaves of bread each put into an oven at time $t = 0$.

(a) Which curve corresponds to the bread that was put into the hottest oven?

(b) Which curve corresponds to the bread that had the lowest temperature at the time that it was put into the oven?

(c) Which two curves correspond to loaves of bread that were at the same temperature when they were put into the oven?

(d) Write a sentence describing any differences between the curves shown in (II) and (III). In terms of bread, what might cause this difference?

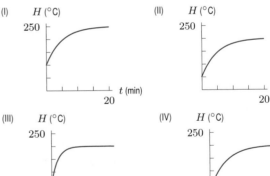

Figure 1.106

23. Sketch reasonable graphs for the following. Pay particular attention to the concavity of the graphs.

(a) The total revenue generated by a car rental business, plotted against the amount spent on advertising.

(b) The temperature of a cup of hot coffee standing in a room, plotted as a function of time.

[78]"Investigating the Next Silent Spring," *US News and World Report*, pp. 50–52 (March 11, 1996).

24. Each of the functions g, h, k in Table 1.42 is increasing, but each increases in a different way. Which of the graphs in Figure 1.107 best fits each function?

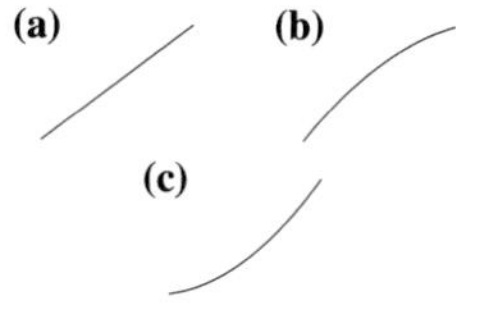

Table 1.42

t	$g(t)$	$h(t)$	$k(t)$
1	23	10	2.2
2	24	20	2.5
3	26	29	2.8
4	29	37	3.1
5	33	44	3.4
6	38	50	3.7

(a)   (b)

(c)

Figure 1.107

25. When a new product is advertised, more and more people try it. However, the rate at which new people try it slows as time goes on.

   (a) Graph the total number of people who have tried such a product against time.

   (b) What do you know about the concavity of the graph?

26. Figure 1.108 shows the age-adjusted death rates from different types of cancer among US males.[79]

   (a) Discuss how the death rate has changed for the different types of cancers.

   (b) For which type of cancer has the average rate of change between 1930 and 1967 been the largest? Estimate the average rate of change for this cancer type. Interpret your answer.

   (c) For which type of cancer has the average rate of change between 1930 and 1967 been the most negative? Estimate the average rate of change for this cancer type. Interpret your answer.

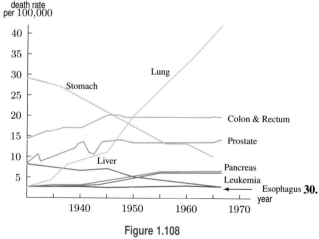

Figure 1.108

27. The volume of water in a pond over a period of 20 weeks is shown in Figure 1.109.

   (a) Is the average rate of change of volume positive or negative over the following intervals?

     (i) $t = 0$ and $t = 5$ (ii) $t = 0$ and $t = 10$
     (iii) $t = 0$ and $t = 15$ (iv) $t = 0$ and $t = 20$

   (b) During which of the following time intervals was the average rate of change larger?

     (i) $0 \le t \le 5$ or $0 \le t \le 10$

     (ii) $0 \le t \le 10$ or $0 \le t \le 20$

   (c) Estimate the average rate of change between $t = 0$ and $t = 10$. Interpret your answer in terms of water.

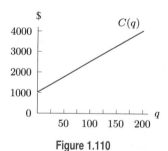

Figure 1.109

28. Find the average rate of change between $x = 0$ and $x = 10$ of each of the following functions: $y = x$, $y = x^2$, $y = x^3$, and $y = x^4$. Which has the largest average rate of change? Graph the four functions, and draw lines whose slopes represent these average rates of change.

29. **(a)** What are the fixed costs and the marginal cost for the cost function in Figure 1.110?

   (b) Explain what $C(100) = 2500$ tells you about costs.

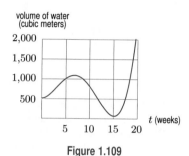

Figure 1.110

30. The Quick-Food company provides a college meal-service plan. Quick-Food has fixed costs of $350,000 per term and variable costs of $400 per student. Quick-Food charges $800 per student per term. How many students must sign up with the Quick-Food plan in order for the company to make a profit?

[79] Abraham M. Lilienfeld, *Foundations of Epidemiology*, p. 67 (New York; Oxford University Press, 1976).

31. For tax purposes, you may have to report the value of your assets, such as cars or refrigerators. The value you report drops with time. "Straight-line depreciation" assumes that the value is a linear function of time. If a $950 refrigerator depreciates completely in seven years, find a formula for its value as a function of time.

32. One of the graphs in Figure 1.111 is a supply curve, and the other is a demand curve. Which is which? Explain how you made your decision using what you know about the effect of price on supply and demand.

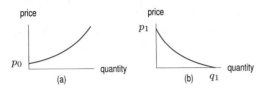

Figure 1.111

33. Figure 1.112 shows supply and demand curves.

(a) What is the equilibrium price for this product? At this price, what quantity is produced?

(b) Choose a price above the equilibrium price—for example, $p = 300$. At this price, how many items are suppliers willing to produce? How many items do consumers want to buy? Use your answers to these questions to explain why, if prices are above the equilibrium price, the market tends to push prices lower (toward the equilibrium).

(c) Now choose a price below the equilibrium price—for example, $p = 200$. At this price, how many items are suppliers willing to produce? How many items do consumers want to buy? Use your answers to these questions to explain why, if prices are below the equilibrium price, the market tends to push prices higher (toward the equilibrium).

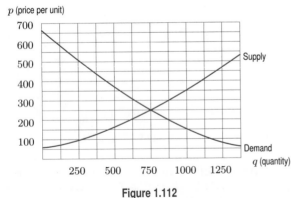

Figure 1.112

Find possible formulas for the graphs in Problems 34–39.

34.

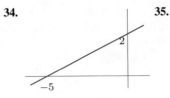

35.

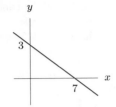

36.

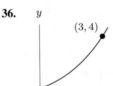

37.

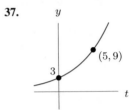

38.

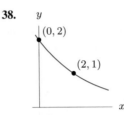

39.

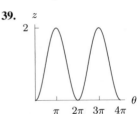

40. The worldwide carbon dioxide emission[80], C, from consumption of fossil fuels was 22.0 billion tons in 1995 and 28.2 billion tons in 2005. Find a formula for the emission C in t years after 1995 if:

(a) C is a linear function of t. What is the annual rate of increase in carbon dioxide emission?

(b) C is an exponential function of t. What is the annual percent rate of increase in carbon dioxide emission?

41. Table 1.43 gives values for three functions. Which functions could be linear? Which could be exponential? Which are neither? For those which could be linear or exponential, give a possible formula for the function.

Table 1.43

x	$f(x)$	$g(x)$	$h(x)$
0	25	30.8	15,000
1	20	27.6	9,000
2	14	24.4	5,400
3	7	21.2	3,240

For Problems 42–45, solve for x using logs.

42. $3^x = 11$

43. $20 = 50(1.04)^x$

44. $e^{5x} = 100$

45. $25e^{3x} = 10$

---

[80]*Statistical Abstracts of the United States 2009*, Table 1304.

46. Write the exponential functions $P = e^{0.08t}$ and $Q = e^{-0.3t}$ in the form $P = a^t$ and $Q = b^t$.

47. (a) What is the continuous percent growth rate for the function $P = 10e^{0.15t}$?
(b) Write this function in the form $P = P_0a^t$.
(c) What is the annual (not continuous) percent growth rate for this function?
(d) Graph $P = 10e^{0.15t}$ and your answer to part (b) on the same axes. Explain what you see.

48. You need $10,000 in your account 3 years from now and the interest rate is 8% per year, compounded continuously. How much should you deposit now?

49. If Q_0 is the quantity of radioactive carbon-14 in an organism at the time of death, the quantity, Q, remaining t years later is given by

$$Q = Q_0e^{-0.000121t}.$$

(a) A skull uncovered at an archeological dig has 15% of the original amount of carbon-14 present. Estimate its age.
(b) Calculate the half-life of carbon-14.

50. A radioactive substance has a half-life of 8 years. If 200 grams are present initially, how much remains at the end of 12 years? How long until only 10% of the original amount remains?

51. The size of an exponentially growing bacteria colony doubles in 5 hours. How long will it take for the number of bacteria to triple?

52. When the Olympic Games were held outside Mexico City in 1968, there was much discussion about the effect the high altitude (7340 feet) would have on the athletes. Assuming air pressure decays exponentially by 0.4% every 100 feet, by what percentage is air pressure reduced by moving from sea level to Mexico City?

53. You have the option of renewing the service contract on your three-year old dishwasher. The new service contract is for three years at a price of $200. The interest rate is 7.25% per year, compounded annually, and you estimate that the costs of repairs if you do not buy the service contract will be $50 at the end of the first year, $100 at the end of the second year, and $150 at the end of the third year. Should you buy the service contract? Explain.

54. If $h(x) = x^3 + 1$ and $g(x) = \sqrt{x}$, find
(a) $g(h(x))$ (b) $h(g(x))$
(c) $h(h(x))$ (d) $g(x) + 1$
(e) $g(x + 1)$

55. Let $f(x) = 2x + 3$ and $g(x) = \ln x$. Find formulas for each of the following functions.
(a) $g(f(x))$ (b) $f(g(x))$ (c) $f(f(x))$

In Problems 56–59, use Figure 1.113 to graph the functions.

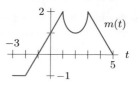

Figure 1.113

56. $n(t) = m(t) + 2$
57. $p(t) = m(t - 1)$
58. $k(t) = m(t + 1.5)$
59. $w(t) = m(t - 0.5) - 2.5$

In Problems 60–62, use Figure 1.114 to graph the function.

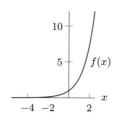

Figure 1.114

60. $5f(x)$ **61.** $f(x + 5)$ **62.** $f(x) + 5$

63. A plan is adopted to reduce the pollution in a lake to the legal limit. The quantity Q of pollutants in the lake after t weeks of clean-up is modeled by the function $Q = f(t)$ where $f(t) = A + Be^{Ct}$.

(a) What are the signs of A, B and C?
(b) What is the initial quantity of pollution in the lake?
(c) What is the legal limit of pollution in the lake?

In Problems 64–65, use shifts of a power function to find a possible formula for the graph.

64. 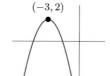   **65.**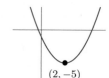

66. The following table gives values for a function $p = f(t)$. Could p be proportional to t?

t	0	10	20	30	40	50
p	0	25	60	100	140	200

67. Zipf's Law, developed by George Zipf in 1949, states that in a given country, the population of a city is inversely proportional to the city's rank by size in the country.[81] Assuming Zipf's Law:

  (a) Write a formula for the population, P, of a city as a function of its rank, R.
  (b) If the constant of proportionality k is 300,000, what is the approximate population of the largest city (rank 1)? The second largest city (rank 2)? The third largest city?
  (c) Answer the questions of part (b) if $k = 6$ million.
  (d) Interpret the meaning of the constant of proportionality k in this context.

Find the period and amplitude in Problems 68–70.

68. $y = 7\sin(3t)$

69. $z = 3\cos(u/4) + 5$

70. $r = 0.1\sin(\pi t) + 2$

71. Figure 1.115 shows the number of reported[82] cases of mumps by month, in the US, for 1972–73.

  (a) Find the period and amplitude of this function, and interpret each in terms of mumps.
  (b) Predict the number of cases of mumps 30 months and 45 months after January 1, 1972.

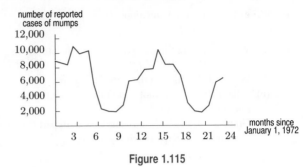

Figure 1.115

72. A population of animals varies periodically between a low of 700 on January 1 and a high of 900 on July 1. Graph the population against time.

For Problems 73–74, find a possible formula for each graph.

73.
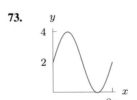

74.
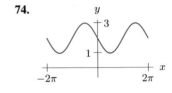

CHECK YOUR UNDERSTANDING

In Problems 1–105, indicate whether the statement is true or false.

  1. The domain is the set of outputs of a function.

  2. If $V = f(a)$, where V is the value of a car (in thousands of dollars) and a is the car's age (in years), then $f(10)$ is the age of a car valued at $10,000.

  3. If $f(x) = x^2$, then the point $(2, 4)$ is on the graph of $f(x)$.

  4. The set of numbers between 3 and 4, including 3 and 4, is written $(3, 4)$.

  5. The function $D = f(r)$ given by $D = -3r + 10$ has vertical intercept 10.

  6. A function is always given by a formula.

  7. If $f(x) = x^2 + 2x + 1$ then $f(3) = 16$.

  8. The graph of a function can have more than one horizontal intercept.

  9. The graph of a function can have more than one vertical intercept.

  10. The vertical intercept on the graph of $C = f(q)$, where C is the cost to produce q items, represents the cost to produce no items.

  11. The slope of the graph of a linear function $f(p)$ is $(f(p_2) - f(p_1))/(p_2 - p_1)$.

  12. The graph of the linear function with formula $m(x) = 3x + 2$ has slope 2.

  13. The slope of the graph of a linear function can be zero.

  14. An equation of a line with slope -1 that passes through the point $(2, 5)$ is $y = -x + 7$.

  15. The function whose values are shown in the following table could be linear:

s	2	4	6	8
$h(s)$	-1	-5	-9	-13

---

[81] Strogatz, S., "Math and the City", The New York Times, May 20, 2009.

[82] Center for Disease Control, 1974, *Reported Morbidity and Mortality in the United States 1973*, Vol. 22, No. 53. Prior to the licensing of the vaccine in 1967, 100,000–200,000 cases of mumps were reported annually. Since 1995, fewer than 1000 cases are reported annually. Source: CDC.

16. The graphs of two different linear functions must intersect in a point.

17. A line with positive slope must also have a positive y-intercept.

18. The linear function $f(x)$ with $f(4) = 2$ and $f(9) = 3$ has slope 5.

19. If number of acres of harvested land is a linear function of elevation in meters, the units of the slope are meters per acre.

20. If $(2, 5)$ is a point on the graph of a line with slope 3, then $(3, 8)$ is also a point on the line.

21. The function $D = f(r)$ given by $D = -3r + 10$ is an increasing function of r.

22. The average rate of change of a linear function $f(t)$ between $t = a$ and $t = b$ is $(f(b) - f(a))/(b - a)$.

23. If $C(n)$ is the total cost, in dollars, to feed n students in the campus cafeteria, then the average rate of change of $C(n)$ has units of students per dollar.

24. If $s(z) = z^2$, then the average rate of change between $z = -1$ and $z = 2$ is positive.

25. A function $f(x)$ can be both increasing and concave down over the interval $0 \le x \le 1$.

26. The function $Q(r)$ given in the following table appears to be concave up:

r	1	2	3	4
$Q(r)$	10	15	17	18

27. The speed and velocity of a moving object are the same.

28. The average rate of change of a function is the slope of the line between two points on the graph of the function.

29. A particle whose position s, in feet, at time t, in seconds, is given by $s(t) = 3t + 2$ has average velocity 3 feet per second.

30. If the graph of a function is concave up, the function must be increasing.

31. The relative change in a quantity is the change divided by the size of the quantity before the change.

32. If production is measured in tons, the units of the percent change of production is also measured in tons.

33. If cost is $1000 for a quantity of 500 and percent change is 15% when the quantity increases by 100 units, then the cost to produce 600 units is $1150.

34. Relative change is always positive.

35. If P in grams is a function of t in hours, then the relative rate of change is measured in grams per hour.

36. Profit is the sum of cost and revenue.

37. Revenue from selling a product is the selling price times the quantity sold.

38. The graph of the cost function $C(q)$ always passes through the origin.

39. The cost function $C(q)$ is a decreasing function of quantity q.

40. If the selling price is constant, the revenue function $R(q)$ is an increasing function of quantity q.

41. Demand is always greater than supply.

42. At equilibrium price p^* and quantity q^*, the supply and demand curves intersect.

43. The units of marginal cost are the same as the units of marginal revenue.

44. The marginal profit is the marginal revenue minus the marginal cost.

45. The imposition of a sales tax won't change the equilibrium price and quantity.

46. The function $Q(t) = 5 \cdot 3^t$ is exponential.

47. An exponential function has a constant percent growth or decay rate.

48. Exponential functions are always increasing.

49. The function $P(t) = 10 \cdot (1.03)^t$ has a 30% growth rate.

50. The function $Q(x) = 35(1/3)^x$ has $Q(2)/Q(1) = 1/3$.

51. The function $R(s) = 16 \cdot 5^s$ has a vertical intercept of 16.

52. The number e satisfies $2 < e < 3$.

53. The function $f(t) = 5^t$ grows more quickly than the function $g(t) = e^t$.

54. If $P = 25(1.15)^t$ gives the size of a population in year t, then the population is growing by 15% per year.

55. The function $Q(r)$ given in the following table could be exponential:

r	0	0.1	0.2	0.3
$Q(r)$	5	6.2	7.4	8.6

56. The value of $\ln(0)$ is 1.

57. The value of $\ln(1)$ is 0.

58. For all $a > 0$ and $b > 0$, we have $\ln(a + b) = \ln(a) \cdot \ln(b)$.

59. The value of $\ln(e^2)$ is 2.

60. The function $f(x) = \ln(x)$ is an increasing function of x.

61. If $5^t = 36$, then $t \ln 5 = \ln 36$.

62. The function $P = 10e^{5t}$ is an exponential growth function.

63. When $b > 0$, we have $e^{\ln b} = \ln(e^b)$.

64. When $B > 0$, we have $\ln(2B) = 2\ln(B)$.

65. When $A > 0$ and $B > 0$, we have $\ln(A^B) = B\ln(A)$.

66. The doubling time of $P(t) = 3e^{5t}$ and $Q(t) = 6e^{5t}$ is the same.

67. If the half-life of a quantity is 6 years, then 100 mg of the substance will decay to 25 mg in 9 years.

68. The half-life of $P(t) = 2e^{-0.6t}$ is twice the half-life of $Q(t) = e^{-0.6t}$.

69. An amount of $1000 invested in a bank account at an interest rate of 3% compounded annually has a balance after t years of $1000e^{0.03t}$.

70. The doubling time of a continuous rate of 6% is more than the doubling time of a continuous rate of 3%.

71. To find the doubling time of $P(t) = 5e^{2t}$, we can solve $10 = 5e^{2t}$ for t.

72. Present value is always less than future value if interest rates are greater than zero.

73. Assuming continuous growth rate of 3%, the future value five years from now of a $1000 payment today is $1000e^{0.15}$.

74. The future value in five years of a $1000 payment made today is less than its future value in ten years (assuming an annual interest rate of 2%).

75. The present value of a payment of $1000 five years from now is less than the present value of a $1000 payment made ten years from now (assuming an annual interest rate of 2%).

76. The graph of $f(x + 5)$ is the same as the graph of $f(x) + 5$.

77. If the graph of $f(x)$ is always increasing, then so is the graph of $f(x + k)$.

78. If the graph of $g(t)$ is concave up, then the graph of $-2g(t)$ is concave down.

79. If the graph of $f(x)$ crosses the x-axis at $x = 1$, then so does the graph of $5f(x)$.

80. If the graph of $f(x)$ crosses the x-axis at $x = 1$, then the graph of $f(x + 1)$ crosses the x-axis at $x = 0$.

81. If $g(s) = s^2$ then $g(3 + h) = 9 + h^2$.

82. If $f(t) = t^2$ and $g(t) = t + 1$ then $f(g(t)) = g(f(t))$.

83. If $f(x) = x^3 - 5$ and $g(x) = \ln x$ then $f(g(x)) = (\ln x)^3 - 5$.

84. The function $h(x) = (3x^2 + 2)^3$ can be written $g(u(x))$ where $g(t) = t^3$ and $u(x) = 3x^2 + 2$.

85. If $f(x) = x^2 - 1$ then $f(x + h) - f(x) = h^2$.

86. If A is proportional to B, then $A = kB$ for some nonzero constant k.

87. If A is inversely proportional to B, then $A = -kB$ for some nonzero constant k.

88. The function $f(x) = 3x^{10}$ is a power function.

89. The function $h(s) = 3 \cdot 10^s$ is a power function.

90. The function $h(x) = 3/\sqrt{x}$ can be written as a power function in the form $h(x) = 3x^{-2}$.

91. The function $g(x) = 3/(2x^2)$ can be written as a power function in the form $g(x) = 6x^{-2}$.

92. The function $f(x) = (3\sqrt{x})/2$ can be written as the power function $f(x) = 1.5x^{1/2}$.

93. If $w = 10.25r^3$, then w is proportional to the cube of r.

94. If $S = 25/\sqrt[3]{t}$, then S is inversely proportional to the cube root of t.

95. If p is proportional to q, then the ratio p/q is constant.

96. The amplitude of $f(x) = 3\sin x$ is $3/2$.

97. The period of $g(x) = \cos x + 2$ is 2π.

98. The value of $\sin(3t)/\sin(5t)$ is $3/5$.

99. The graph of $y = \cos x$ is a horizontal shift of the graph of $y = \sin x$.

100. The period of $y = 3\cos(5t) + 7$ is 5.

101. The period of $y = \sin(2t)$ is twice the period of $y = \sin(t)$.

102. The functions $f(t) = 5\sin t$ and $g(t) = 8 + 5\sin t$ have the same amplitude.

103. The graphs of $y = (\sin x)^2$ and $y = \sin(x^2)$ are the same.

104. For all x, we have $0 \leq \sin(x) \leq 1$.

105. For all x, we have $\sin^2 x + \cos^2 x = 1$.

PROJECTS FOR CHAPTER ONE

1. Compound Interest

The newspaper article below is from *The New York Times*, May 27, 1990. Fill in the three blanks. (For the first blank, assume that daily compounding is essentially the same as continuous compounding. For the last blank, assume the interest has been compounded yearly, and give your answer in dollars. Ignore the occurrence of leap years.)

213 Years After Loan, Uncle Sam Is Dunned

By LISA BELKIN

Special to The New York Times

SAN ANTONIO, May 26 — More than 200 years ago, a wealthy Pennsylvania merchant named Jacob DeHaven lent $450,000 to the Continental Congress to rescue the troops at Valley Forge. That loan was apparently never repaid.

So Mr. DeHaven's descendants are taking the United States Government to court to collect what they believe they are owed.

The total: ____ in today's dollars if the interest is compounded daily at 6 percent, the going rate at the time. If compounded yearly, the bill is only ____.

Family Is Flexible

The descendants say that they are willing to be flexible about the amount of a settlement and that they might even accept a heartfelt thank you or perhaps a DeHaven statue. But they also note that interest is accumulating at ____ a second.

2. Population Center of the US

Since the opening up of the West, the US population has moved westward. To observe this, we look at the "population center" of the US, which is the point at which the country would balance if it were a flat plate with no weight, and every person had equal weight. In 1790 the population center was east of Baltimore, Maryland. It has been moving westward ever since, and in 2000 it was in Edgar Springs, Missouri. During the second half of the 20th century, the population center has moved about 50 miles west every 10 years.

(a) Let us measure position westward from Edgar Springs along the line running through Baltimore. For the years since 2000, express the approximate position of the population center as a function of time in years from 2000.

(b) The distance from Baltimore to Edgar Springs is a bit over 1000 miles. Could the population center have been moving at roughly the same rate for the last two centuries?

(c) Could the function in part (a) continue to apply for the next four centuries? Why or why not? [Hint: You may want to look at a map. Note that distances are in air miles and are not driving distances.]

Chapter Two

RATE OF CHANGE: THE DERIVATIVE

Contents

2.1 Instantaneous Rate of Change **88**

Instantaneous Velocity 88

Defining Instantaneous Velocity Using the
Idea of a Limit 89

Instantaneous Rate of Change 89

The Derivative at a Point 90

Visualizing the Derivative: Slope of the Graph
and Slope of the Tangent Line 90

Estimating the Derivative of a Function Given
Numerically 92

2.2 The Derivative Function **95**

Finding the Derivative of a Function Given
Graphically 95

What Does the Derivative Tell Us Graphically? 97

Estimating the Derivative of a Function Given
Numerically 97

Improving Numerical Estimates . . . 98

Finding the Derivative of a Function Given by
a Formula 98

2.3 Interpretations of the Derivative **101**

An Alternative Notation for the Derivative . . 101

Using Units to Interpret the Derivative 102

Using the Derivative to Estimate Values of a
Function 104

Relative Rate of Change 105

2.4 The Second Derivative **110**

What Does the Second Derivative Tell Us? . . 110

Interpretation of the Second Derivative as a
Rate of Change 111

2.5 Marginal Cost and Revenue **115**

Graphs of Cost and Revenue Functions . . . 115

Marginal Analysis 116

REVIEW PROBLEMS **121**

CHECK YOUR UNDERSTANDING **124**

**PROJECTS: Estimating Temperature of a Yam,
Temperature and Illumination** **125**

**Limits, Continuity, and the Definition of the
Derivative** **127**

Definition of the Derivative Using Average Rates 127

The Idea of a Limit 128

Continuity 129

Using the Definition to Calculate Derivatives . 130

2.1 INSTANTANEOUS RATE OF CHANGE

Chapter 1 introduced the average rate of change of a function over an interval. In this section, we consider the rate of change of a function at a point. We saw in Chapter 1 that when an object is moving along a straight line, the average rate of change of position with respect to time is the average velocity. If position is expressed as $y = f(t)$, where t is time, then

$$\text{Average rate of change in position between } t = a \text{ and } t = b \quad = \frac{\Delta y}{\Delta t} = \frac{f(b) - f(a)}{b - a}.$$

If you drive 200 miles in 4 hours, your average velocity is $200/4 = 50$ miles per hour. Of course, this does not mean that you travel at exactly 50 mph the entire trip. Your velocity at a given instant during the trip is shown on your speedometer, and this is the quantity that we investigate now.

Instantaneous Velocity

We throw a grapefruit straight upward into the air. Table 2.1 gives its height, y, at time t. What is the velocity of the grapefruit at exactly $t = 1$? We use average velocities to estimate this quantity.

Table 2.1   *Height of the grapefruit above the ground*

t (sec)	0	1	2	3	4	5	6
$y = s(t)$ (feet)	6	90	142	162	150	106	30

The average velocity on the interval $0 \le t \le 1$ is 84 ft/sec and the average velocity on the interval $1 \le t \le 2$ is 52 ft/sec. Notice that the average velocity before $t = 1$ is larger than the average velocity after $t = 1$ since the grapefruit is slowing down. We expect the velocity *at $t = 1$* to be between these two average velocities. How can we find the velocity at *exactly $t = 1$*? We look at what happens near $t = 1$ in more detail. Suppose that we find the average velocities on either side of $t = 1$ over smaller and smaller intervals, as in Figure 2.1. Then, for example,

$$\text{Average velocity between } t = 1 \text{ and } t = 1.01 \quad = \frac{\Delta y}{\Delta t} = \frac{s(1.01) - s(1)}{1.01 - 1} = \frac{90.678 - 90}{0.01} = 67.8 \text{ ft/sec.}$$

We expect the instantaneous velocity at $t = 1$ to be between the average velocities on either side of $t = 1$. In Figure 2.1, the values of the average velocity before $t = 1$ and the average velocity after $t = 1$ get closer together as the size of the interval shrinks. For the smallest intervals in Figure 2.1, both velocities are 68.0 ft/sec (to one decimal place), so we say the velocity at $t = 1$ is 68.0 ft/sec (to one decimal place).

t	0	0.9	0.99	0.999	1	1.001	1.01	1.1	2
$y = s(t)$	6.000	83.040	89.318	89.932	90.000	90.068	90.678	96.640	142.000

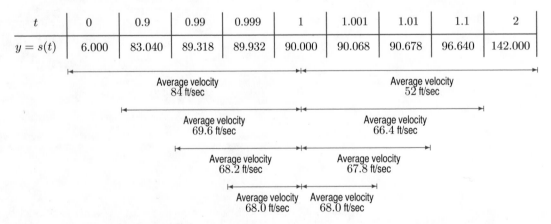

Figure 2.1: Average velocities over intervals on either side of $t = 1$ showing successively smaller intervals